S0-AHI-812

Folk and Fairy Tales
of Far-off Lands

Folk and Fairy Tales of Far-off Lands

edited and adapted by
ERIC *and* **NANCY PROTTER**

introduction by **R. V. CASSILL**
translation by **ROBERT EGAN**
illustrated by **DOROTHY E. ROSENWASSER**
DUELL, SLOAN *and* **PEARCE   NEW YORK**

COPYRIGHT © 1965 BY ERIC PROTTER
*All rights reserved. No part of this book in excess
of five hundred words may be reproduced in any form
without permission in writing from the publisher.*

FIRST EDITION

DUELL, SLOAN & PEARCE
AFFILIATE OF
MEREDITH PRESS

Library of Congress Catalog Card Number: 65-26811
MANUFACTURED IN THE UNITED STATES OF AMERICA
FOR MEREDITH PRESS

For Curtis

Acknowledgments

It is with deep gratitude and appreciation that we acknowledge numerous translations by Robert Egan as well as the introduction by R. V. Cassill.

Among the most important works consulted for translation, adaptation or research are: *Folk-Tales of Bengal* by Lal Behari Day, London, 1883; *Ancient Tales and Folklore of Japan* by R. G. Smith, London, 1908; *Das Märchenjahr* by Lisa Tetzner, Munich, 1956; *The Piece of Brocade* by Kan Niu, 1961; *Ozean der Märchenströme* by Braun, Leyden, 1909; *Stories of the Indo-Chinese* by Adolf Bastias, Leipzig, 1866; *Volksmärchen und Volksdichtung Afrikas* by L. Frobenius, Jena, 1921–28; *Afrikanische Märchen* by C. Meinhof, Jena, 1921; *Mythology of All Nations* by A. Werner, Boston, 1920; *Garten der Erde* by Wilhelm Schmidtbonn, n.d.; and *Mythologie universelle* by A. H. Krappe, Paris, 1930.

Contents

Introduction

HE DELIGHT WE TAKE FROM FAIRY TALES AND
folk tales comes not so much for their
strangeness as from their familiarity. Of
course they are strange in their circumstances and in their serene disregard for the common
appearances of things. In them animals talk and reason
in ways we consider human. Actions are attributed to
inanimate things. Mirrors, chairs, rugs, brooms, chests,
and doors are said to behave in ways that, for want of
a better word, we call magic. And yet our ability to
believe in the familiar, essential truth of the tales is not
a bit weakened by these departures from the circumstances of the world we see around us.

This is so because the disregard for factual truth
permits another, more fundamental kind of truth to
shine out in unexpected purity and simplicity. We say
that most of these tales have morals. Are we not really
saying that their true subject is a moral reality that
is as easily comprehensible to the intuition of a child
as to an adult?

These are stories of crime and punishment, wish and
reward, desire and transgression. The marvelous con-
vention of calling the criminal a tiger, for instance, or

attributing a beautiful wish to some frail creature of the woods, shows crime and hope in the aura of wonder which we associate with the ageless wisdom of the race. The tales remind us of what we always knew—that humans are part of the natural world. By asserting our kinship with it we see our human qualities reflected in clear outline.

Truly such stories are timeless. The "once upon a time" of a fairy tale is always "now"—and in the spell of the stories the present moments of our lives are transformed into "once upon a time." In this collection, drawn from the joy and wisdom of people around the earth, imagination wipes out the boundaries of space. The little corners we inhabit are opened to the world.

R. V. CASSILL

Folk and Fairy Tales
of Far-off Lands

The Girl in the Moon

An unusual tale from the South Seas—a combination of folklore and fairy tale.

ANY, MANY YEARS AGO, WHEN THE WORLD was quite different from its present state, and the spirits were still on friendly terms with mankind, a young girl lived with her grandmother on the lovely little island of Wauhu. They made their home beneath an enormous tree, whose topmost branches reached the heavens. Its leaves were glossy green and so thick that the sun's rays could not pass through them. Thus nature provided the girl and her grandmother with a wonderful roof over their heads, protecting them from the rains.

In time, when the granddaughter grew to young womanhood, the grandmother said to herself, "Soon Wanhoko must choose a husband." Sighing, she pondered, "But where is one to be found?"

One day she called her granddaughter to her.

"My good child," she said, "the time has come when you must start to think about getting married. You are so pretty that there will be many men who will brave fire and water for your hand. The truth is, however, that I have already chosen someone for you. Go to bed now, because tomorrow you must rise before daybreak."

The next morning the grandmother carefully instructed her granddaughter on what she should wear. First rimming the young girl's hair with flowers, she then placed a garland of beautiful blossoms around her neck. Afterward Wanhoko anointed herself with fragrant oils and perfumes. When all was properly done, she was told to climb to the top of the tree under which they lived.

"You know," said the grandmother, "that the branches of this tree are rungs that ascend to the heavens. No one has dared to go up them, for whoever does will surely die. Yet do not fear. I will cast a magic spell upon you that will protect you from any harm. Do as I say and all will be well."

"Grandmother," replied Wanhoko, "I will go wherever you wish without fear, for I know that all you do is for my sake."

After the grandmother had pronounced her magic spell, they both lay on their mats and went to sleep.

The next morning before the sun rose, Wanhoko, adorned with beautiful flowers and scented with fragrant oils, stood at the foot of the lofty tree.

"My dearest child," said the grandmother, embracing her tenderly, "if you return, I shall be happy; if not, I shall know that you are in good hands."

Now the granddaughter climbed the branches of the tree quickly and confidently, protected from any hazard by the magic spell.

When she reached the topmost limbs, she beheld a little house. Sitting near it was an old blind woman. She was busy making palm wine into syrup by boiling it in coconut shells over hot stones. She stirred the liquid vigorously to prevent the syrup from burning. While she worked, she sang. And every once in a while she would count the coconut shells with great care.

Wanhoko decided to play a game with her. Each

time the old woman would finish counting the shells, the young girl would remove one quickly. The next time the woman would count, there would be another shell missing. The old woman soon realized that the shells were diminishing so rapidly that something odd was taking place.

"Fewer and fewer shells!" she cried. "They can't run away by themselves!" Suddenly her arm shot out and she caught Wanhoko right in the act of stealing a coconut bowl.

"Aha, I've caught you!" exclaimed the old woman triumphantly. "You scamp. Stealing from a blind woman, indeed. You'll pay dearly for this, I wager. My children will kill you when they hear how you have wronged their mother."

"Oh," sobbed Wanhoko, terrified. "Please be merciful. I just did it for a lark. Forgive me, please. I'll never do it again."

Wanhoko begged the old woman to let go of her arm, but she only clutched it tighter.

"My name is Burana," said the old woman. "I am the mother of the sun and the moon. I was making syrup, as I do every morning. Now, thanks to you, I have nothing to make it with. You've stolen all my shells, you naughty girl."

"Oh, sweet Burana, please let me go. I will do anything for you. I will become your faithful servant," pleaded the girl.

"What would I do with a servant?" retorted the old lady. "Everything I do, I do out of love for my children." Dismissing the idea with a gesture, she said, "As for myself, I do not need food, drink, or sleep."

"Dear Burana, please release me," implored the maiden once again. "If you set me free I will tell you a secret that my grandmother imparted to me."

"All right, you silly girl," said the old woman, loosening her grip slightly. "What is it?"

"I can heal your blindness."

Burana at once let go of the girl.

Placing the worn face of the old woman between her

hands, Wanhoko murmured several secret words; and then, taking two teardrops from her own eyes, she touched the old woman's lids with them. Instantly the lids drew back, exposing eyes dusted with a gray mist. Taking two more teardrops, the young girl placed one drop on each iris. Immediately, the mist over the eyes dissolved and in a brilliant flash the old woman's sight was restored.

Burana's joy was beyond bounds. Clapping her hands, she danced wildly about, exclaiming, "What a glorious world! What a glorious world! I always thought it was so dark and hideous. Such colors!" Crying with happiness, she said, "Now I can finally see the faces of my children."

Suddenly she stopped and regarded Wanhoko. "My dear child, I'm sorry. I was so overwhelmed with joy that I forgot about you. If I do not hide you instantly, my children will return and certainly kill you." She added darkly, "They kill everyone they meet."

Carefully she secreted Wanhoko underneath a great hollow trough.

"My dear," she warned, "you must remain absolutely still. The sun and the moon will be here in a minute."

The old woman's warning came not a minute too soon. Immediately the sun appeared and dazzled the old woman's eyes to such an extent that she had to turn her face away.

The sun, seeing this, said, "Mother, why do you turn your face from me? You never did that before."

"Ah my child, for the very first time I can *see* you!"

"How is that possible, Mother?" asked the sun. "Who has worked such a miracle?"

At that moment the moon appeared. The mother noticed his soft radiance and compared it to the harsh
brilliance of the sun, whose light she could not face.

The moon came to his mother and said, "Why do you
look upon us so strangely, Mother, as if you could
really see us?"

"My son," cried the old woman happily, "I *do* see
you! I can peer into your face." Then she said somewhat sadly, "But, my offspring, the sun dazzles me so
much that I cannot look upon him."

"Mother dear," said the moon, "what is that fra-
grance? It smells of humankind."

"And so it is, my child," replied the old woman.
"Close by there is a darling, lovely maiden adorned
with roses and filled with love. It is she who has cured
my blindness. She is so charming and beautiful that I
think one of you should marry her."

"Oh, Mother," the sun and the moon replied in
unison, "ask her to come forward and choose between
us. Whatever her choice, we shall not be jealous."

Reassured by this promise, Burana then went to the
hollow trough and revealed the radiant Wanhoko. Taking her by the hand, she presented the young girl to her
children.

"Now, child," she said, "both my sons wish you for
their bride. Whom do you consider for your husband?"

Wanhoko reflected for many moments. Glancing
back and forth from one to the other, she at last made
her decision.

"I cannot marry the sun," she said softly. "He is so
brilliant that I cannot look directly into his face."
Turning to the moon, she said, "The moon, on the other

hand, seems gentle and serene. My choice falls upon the gentle moon. I wish to be *his* wife.''

At these words the moon approached the maiden, and bearing her aloft, carried her into the cool skies forever.

The Iron-Eating Mice

A man trying to cheat a neighbor is taught a lesson in this popular folk tale from Turkestan.

N A SMALL TOWN IN TURKESTAN, THERE ONCE lived a shopkeeper who was having a very bad time of it. Business was so terrible that he decided to close up shop and try another area altogether. After disposing of all his goods, he was left with only one piece of equipment— an iron scale for weighing vegetables. Resolving to store the scale, he went to his friend, the farmer, and asked him if he would keep the object for him until he returned. Happy to oblige, the farmer placed the scale in his cellar.

Off the merchant went to try his luck elsewhere, but he soon found that business was just as bad in the new place, so before long he returned home.

Once again in town, he busied himself getting his shop ready. At last, nearly everything was in place. After paying a call on his old friend, the merchant thanked the farmer for keeping the scale and told him that he had come to take it back.

"Oh, I'm afraid that's impossible," said the farmer.

"Why is that?" asked the surprised merchant.

"Because the mice have eaten it."

"Eaten the scale? But it's made of iron!" he exclaimed.

"Nevertheless it's true," stated the farmer blandly.

The merchant, suspecting correctly that the farmer was trying to outwit him and had plans to sell the scale elsewhere, decided not to press the point.

"Well!" he murmured. "This certainly makes my situation difficult. I wonder, my friend," he said casually, "do you think your son might help me carry some merchandise into the store tomorrow?"

The farmer, relieved to have gotten away with the scale trick so easily, was happy to lend his son to the merchant for a few hours' work.

"Certainly, certainly, my dear friend," he said. Calling his son, he instructed him to go to the merchant's shop the following morning.

The next day, after the young boy had carried a few sacks of grain from one side of the shop to the other, the merchant told him to rest. He gave the boy a few games to play with and told him to stay where he was and not to worry. He locked the door and hurried off to the farmer.

Seeing the shopkeeper approaching without his son, the farmer immediately inquired as to his whereabouts.

"I'm dreadfully sorry to be the bearer of bad news," declared the merchant. "Just as your son was toting a sack of rice, a wild duck flew over my house. Before I knew it, the bird swooped down and abducted your dear, sweet child. It all happened before my very eyes."

Hearing this, the farmer grew livid with rage.

"What kind of a story is this?" he demanded. "If you don't tell me the truth immediately, I'll take you to court."

Although he protested loudly that everything he had

said had actually happened, the merchant was nevertheless taken to court by the farmer.

Once in front of the judge, both men told their
stories.

"Your Honor," said the farmer, "this man, who pro-
fesses to be my friend, has kidnapped my son."

"Where is the boy?" asked the judge, addressing the
merchant.

"A duck abducted him," replied the merchant without batting an eyelash.

"What in the world do you mean by that?" demanded the judge. "That's absolutely impossible. How
can a small duck carry off a fourteen-year-old boy?"

"Oh, my dear judge," replied the merchant politely, "though I certainly do not want to contradict you, it is important for me to tell you that if in this world of ours mice are able to eat iron scales, then certainly small ducks can carry off big boys."

"What!" shrieked the judge, offended at this new outrage. "Mice eating iron, did you say?"

"Yes, Your Honor, it's quite true." Immediately he told the judge the farmer's story of the scale.

"I see . . ." said the judge, instantly realizing what had really happened.

The farmer, realizing also that the merchant had known all along of his deception, now hung his head in shame.

"My friend," he finally said to the merchant, "I have truly learned my lesson. Please allow me to make amends. First I shall return your scale. Then, if you will let me, I would like to assist you in getting your business started again. Let us be friends once more."

The merchant, a good-natured man who was quite willing to let bygones by bygones, agreed to the suggestion. From then on and for the rest of their days, the farmer and the merchant remained on good terms, and never again did the farmer try to swindle anyone.

The Walnut Thieves

In this humorous tale from Niger, two of the weaker members of the animal world outwit their powerful neighbors.

 HERE ONCE WAS A TIGER MANY, MANY YEARS ago who had in his domain a great walnut tree. Since he was very greedy, he proclaimed to all the other beasts that if they stole any of his walnuts they would pay for it with their lives. This warning applied to the tortoise as well, but as he was thick-shelled and well protected, he didn't take the threat too seriously.

One day, when the walnuts were deliciously ripe and the branches were bending low under their weight, the tortoise visited his good friend, the dog. They were discussing the hard conditions of the times when the tortoise suddenly said, "Dear friend, did you know that the walnuts on the tiger's tree are now ripe? Don't you sometimes long for just one taste of that delicious fruit?"

"I'll admit quite frankly," confessed the dog, "that for some time I have been looking at them quite longingly." Glancing sideways at the tortoise, he suggested, "If you were to accompany me there one fine day, I would have the benefit of your advice at every moment."

14

"Most certainly," enthused the tortoise. "We can go there the first thing tomorrow morning. However, as you know, early rising is my weak point, so perhaps you'd better come by and wake me up."

The following morning at the appointed hour, the dog pounded on the tortoise's door.

"I'm coming," called the tortoise, tucking an old bag under his arm. They walked side by side in silence for some distance, when all at once the tortoise said, "I must remind you that sometimes the walnuts will fall on your head and hurt you dreadfully. You must give me your solemn word that you will not cry out in pain. Just say these secret words: 'Oomph, oomph, poobu, bu!' It will stop the ache."

Indignantly the dog said, "How dare you think I'd scream! Don't you think that I know, too, that the tiger has ears? Surely he would not hesitate a minute to kill us both!"

"It's all very well for you to be so cocksure of yourself," replied the tortoise, "but if worse comes to worse, you can always run away. But what about poor me? I have such short legs I'd be sure to get caught."

"Now, now, don't worry," soothed the dog. "I promise you on my honor that I won't cry out."

By this time the two friends had arrived beneath the spreading branches of the walnut tree. The tortoise eagerly began gathering the plump walnuts. Joyfully the dog joined him, circling the tree in wild leaps while the tortoise tried to restrain him. Noticing a huge clump of nuts, he rushed over to the low branch and began to shake it vigorously. Immediately a walnut rattled through the limbs and plunked on the back of the tortoise.

"Oomph, oomph, poobu, bu!" recited the tortoise calmly. Then he turned to the dog and said, "Now you see how it's done."

"Yes, yes," replied the dog with irritation. "I quite understand." Bounding away he gave the tree another shattering shake. A huge walnut bounced straight onto the crown of his head.

"Wow ... wow ... wow ... wow!" howled the dog in agony. Throwing his bag of walnuts aside, he swiftly headed for home.

"Good gracious," exclaimed the tortoise with terror, "I'm really done for now." Already he heard the tiger approaching. With great presence of mind he scurried under the dry leaves.

When the tiger appeared, the first thing he saw was the dog's discarded bag of walnuts.

"Aha! Walnut thieves!" snarled the tiger. "You'll pay for this, you scoundrels!" Immediately he began searching for the guilty ones. After an hour he was about to give up, when a little black and yellow bird alighted on a branch and sang a message to him.

"Under the leaves, tiger! Under the leaves!"

An icy chill ran up and down the tortoise's back as the tiger renewed his search.

"Under the leaves, tiger! Under the leaves!" the bird kept chanting.

Unable to find anything, the tiger became infuriated with the bird and hurled a stick at it. Nimbly it hopped away, but the stick landed on the tortoise's back, forcing him to move near the roots of the tree.

Keeping excellent track of the tortoise, the bird reported his new position.

"Under the roots, tiger! Under the roots!" This time the tiger leaped swiftly to the spot, and removing the

roots, looked directly into the terrified eyes of the tortoise.

"So, Mr. Tortoise, *you* are the thief!" Quickly he removed one of the two bags he carried on his shoulder and began to put the tortoise inside of it.

"Oh, my dear friend," remarked the tortoise, "not in your nice new bag. See how dirty I am. Use the old one instead."

"You're right," admitted the tiger. Placing the tortoise in the old one, he quickly hurried off with his prisoner.

There was cunning in the tortoise's suggestion, for he had noticed that one side of the bag was badly worn. He knew that he could easily pull the bamboo fibers apart. Once inside the bag he quickly worked his way through a hole and hopped out onto the soft grass, leaving his bag of walnuts inside the tiger's sack to add some weight to it.

"The tiger won't take that very lightly when he sees it," laughed the tortoise. Then he returned home to recover from the dangerous experience. When he was thoroughly rested he set off to see his friend the dog to give him a piece of his mind.

When the tiger reached home he gave orders for a pot of water to be placed upon the fire at once. Then he issued invitations to all his friends to attend a feast.

When all the guests had arrived and the pot was boiling vigorously over the fire, the tiger stated with great formality, "I have caught Mr. Tortoise stealing my walnuts. I am very happy that you can all join me in a delectable repast at his expense." All the animals applauded and looked forward eagerly to the coming event. With great ceremony the tiger undid the bag and reached in his paw for the tortoise. To his complete dismay he could not find him. Rummaging around anxiously among the dead leaves and walnuts, he forced them through the hole and one by one they pattered all over the table. Utterly embarrassed about being tricked, the tiger roared with fury.

All the guests began to laugh hilariously. Some of them pounded the tables. Others rolled over on their sides. Some believed the tiger had meant to make fools of them and screamed at the tiger before they left in a rage.

The poor tiger's spirits were very, very low. For days he sulked in his lair. His sons thought that perhaps he was asleep, but they were badly mistaken. He had merely closed his eyes to concentrate more fully on plans for revenge.

Strangely, the friendship of the dog and the tortoise did not suffer in the slightest, despite the walnut episode. They visited back and forth as before and talked often of their ill-fated venture.

The dog spoke regretfully of his behavior.

"If a walnut were to hit me again, I would control myself the way you did," he said. "I'd say those words."

One day, after the dog had repeated this for the twentieth time, the tortoise said, "If I had your solemn promise on it, I might be tempted to give it another try."

"Oh, yes, yes! That's an excellent idea!" agreed the dog, bounding about with delight.

"But if you break your promise," warned the tortoise "a trick won't save me again. I'll be in the soup for sure."

"It saddens me to think that you have no confidence in me," said the dog mournfully.

The tortoise, deeply moved by his friend's sincerity, impulsively asserted that tomorrow morning they would make another attempt at gathering some nuts.

At the first light of dawn the two friends drew near the tree. This time the tortoise had borrowed a very large bag from an acquaintance. Together the friends began to fill the bag. Walnuts were in great abundance everywhere so that the task was not at all difficult. Suddenly there was a familiar clatter in the branches, and the next instant a walnut fell with a dreadful bump onto the dog's back.

"Wow . . . wow . . . wow . . . wow!" shrieked the hound. Howling miserably, he leapt off toward home, leaving the poor tortoise face to face with the angry tiger. Quickly the tiger popped the tortoise into a bag and rushed him home without wasting a minute.

In the meantime the dog had not run far when he turned around just in time to see the tiger disappearing with his friend. Dreadfully conscience-stricken, he decided that he must at all costs save the tortoise.

"I will go to the sorcerer," he thought at once. "He will know what to do."

Fortunately the sorcerer was at home and prepared to give good advice. He brought out several long necklaces of seashells and many large and small bells, and a variety of other articles that jingled, tinkled, clattered, clashed, and clanked. He hung all of these on the dog so that he was no longer recognizable. Lastly he attached a great kettle drum and provided the dog with an enormous pair of drumsticks. Thus fantastically arrayed, the dog was told to sit down.

"Now listen carefully," said the sorcerer. "Go at once as you are to the river and conceal yourself. It won't be long before the tiger and his companions come down to draw some water. When they do, you will know that there is no one in the tiger's house. As soon as you observe them in the distance, start making a dreadful hubbub. When they come nearer, shake and twist and howl and jump like a mad lunatic. None of them will take a chance at drawing water—not even the lion—if they think a monster guards the stream. In the meantime your friend can escape."

The dog was so delighted with this scheme that he wanted to embrace the sorcerer, but the latter warded him off laughingly and advised him to hasten to the river.

The tiger, meanwhile, had arrived home with his catch. The unfortunate tortoise had tried once again to outwit the tiger by begging him to put him in the old bag, but the beast was now too smart to be taken in by this suggestion.

"No, no," he said, "you would surely attempt to escape. With you in the new bag, my mind is at ease."

Prospects for the tortoise were now very dim indeed. With horror he heard the tiger once again extend invitations to all his friends, including the lion and the elephant.

While he waited for all his friends to assemble, the tiger kept a watchful eye upon the tortoise. After they had gathered, he started a crackling fire and called for a pot of water. To his dismay the water pitchers were empty, so he sent his sons down to the river to get some water.

"Quickly, quickly," he said. "We mustn't keep our guests waiting."

All the animals were curious to see the tortoise, so he

was passed from hand to hand while the guests waited for the tiger's sons to return. Suddenly they burst through the door roaring and squealing in such alarm that no one could make head or tail of their story. Gradually calmed, they were at last able to describe what had frightened them.

"There is a most horrible monster down at the river. It screams and shouts and makes such a dreadful racket that we nearly died of fright!"

"What nonsense!" said the tiger reproachfully. While his sons continued to shiver and chatter in the corner of the room, the tiger asked some of his friends to go for the water instead.

It was not long before they too came back in exactly the same state. Quaking with terror they verified the report of the dreadful monster.

Proudly the lion stood up and said, "Enough is enough. *I* shall go down and fetch the water myself." Regally he glided down the hill, pitchers and pots clanking about his shoulders as he moved.

In two minutes he was back, his mane bristling with fright and his eyes quivering with a most dreadful knowledge. All the other animals were seized with renewed fear when the lion gave his account. "In my whole life," he moaned, "nothing, nothing so horrible has ever happened to me! This can only be witchcraft," he asserted. "What I encountered resembled no animal I have ever seen. It was a creature so ghastly that I threw myself down on the ground in panic. Fortunately I was able to regain the use of my legs and I fled swiftly, with the monster in close pursuit."

"But what in the world can it be?" asked the ele-

phant in astonishment. "I doubt if anything in the
world could scare *me!*" Urged on by the others, he
said, "I will go to the river."

"Then go!" said the lion angrily. Throwing the pitchers down on the ground, he smashed and broke them
all.

"You forget," laughed the elephant. "I don't need
such things. I have my trunk." Calmly he strolled off,
while all the animals waited with increasing anxiety.

From far away they suddenly heard the sound of his
mighty trumpet. Hooting all the way up the hill, he
came crashing into the room so distracted with terror
that all the guests were frozen with fear at the sight of
him. They were now convinced that death and destruc-
tion waited for them all at the river.

The tiger was now in an absolute fury. Everyone
spoke of the hideous monster at once, adding to their
descriptions the most abominable details. Some said he
had five legs, others that he had three eyes. Some declared that he was made entirely of metal, others of a
strange mixture of horns and bells. Some insisted that
he spouted fire, while others stated that he gave off a
horrible odor. No two could agree entirely as to what
the grizzly creature really looked like.

The disgusted tiger decided that the only solution to
this mystery was to go and have a look at the monster
himself. Caution, however, intruded upon the tiger's
usual bravery, and he decided that perhaps it was best
not to make the trip to the river all alone. Instead he
rapped on the table for attention and offered a suggestion to all the animals.

"My dear friends," he said. "I thank you all for hon-

oring me with your presence, and for the willingness
you have shown to help me. I don't doubt for a minute
that you have seen some horrible monster. But—I believe since now you are acquainted with it, you are
better prepared to confront it. For this reason,''—here
the tiger stopped and coughed politely behind his paw
—"I would like to offer a suggestion. Let us *all* go
down to the river *together* and attempt to capture and
kill the monster."

At the conclusion of this long speech, there arose
much muttering among the guests. They debated at
length whether they should risk this venture once
again. Some favored the tiger's proposal; others hesitated. Finally the whole group resolved to go along.
With the elephant and the lion in the vanguard, they
all hurried to the river. As far behind as possible
trotted the tiger. Entirely forgotten in the excitement
was the tortoise in the bag. One thought was in the
mind of all: What would they meet at the river?

As soon as the last guest was on his way, the tortoise
swiftly plopped from the bag and journeyed home. Un-
like the rest of the animals, he was not interested in the
adventure. He strongly suspected that the dog had
created the diversion of the monster to set him free. As
he walked along, he became increasingly worried
about his friend's welfare. While it was perfectly possible for the dog to frighten the animals one by one as
they appeared at the river, it was another thing altogether to frighten an army of them. "Oh—woe, woe, to
my poor best and dearest friend if he is recognized!"
cried the tortoise to himself.

As it happened, the tortoise's worries were unfounded. No sooner had he turned a corner in the woods when he came face to face with the dog. Joyously the two friends embraced each other. Then the dog told the tortoise how, as soon as he had seen the body of animals marching determinedly toward the river, he had cleverly sneaked off into the woods. By the time the odd collection of creatures arrived at the bank, all thumping and shouting, there wasn't a monster in sight. Laughing hilariously at the thought of the scene, the two friends rolled upon the ground until exhausted.

At last the dog said seriously, in a faint and ashamed voice, "Please forgive me, my friend, for my bad behavior."

With gentle good nature the tortoise replied, "Let's let bygones be bygones. You have proved yourself a loyal and true friend. However," he chuckled softly, "perhaps, for the sake of our friendship, it would be best if we do not go stealing walnuts together again."

Back at the river bank, the tiger and his companions were absolutely astonished to find no evidence of the horrible monster. The tiger strongly suspected that there never had been a monster in the first place and laughed and laughed at his friends' embarrassment. They, however, had the very last laugh when they all returned to the house of the tiger and he discovered with dismay that his big, fat, delicious tortoise had escaped the soup once more.

The Mirror

Vanity is examined in a unique way in this profoundly moving tale from Japan.

ANY YEARS AGO THERE LIVED IN A REMOTE part of Japan a young man and his good wife. They had one child, a beautiful baby girl, whom they both adored.

One day it became necessary for the husband to make a journey to the capital city, which was very far away. Sadly he made his preparations, for the trip would take several weeks and it was not possible for him to bring his beloved wife and daughter along.

When he parted from his wife he kissed her tenderly and said, "When I return, I shall bring you something very pretty."

The young woman watched him depart with much anxiety. In her whole life, she had never been farther away than the next village. During her husband's long absence she remained quite nervous and frightened.

As the time drew near for him to return she put out for herself and her daughter their finest clothes. For herself she selected a delicate cloud-blue garment for which her husband had a special fondness.

One day her husband appeared at the door. How great was her joy to have him home safe and sound again! Lovingly they embraced one another. Then her

26

husband carefully unpacked the beautiful object which he had promised to bring back with him.

"I have something marvelous for you," he told his wife. "It is a *tagami*—a mirror. Look into it and tell me what you see."

The couple lived in a district so removed from the great world beyond that the young wife had neither heard of nor seen such a thing as a mirror, and in her innocence she did not suspect what it was.

Carefully she opened a carved wooden chest and saw placed within it on a silken cushion a round silver disk. Sculpted upon the disk were handsome figures, flowers, and birds. When she picked up the object and turned it over, she was astonished to see a brightly polished surface reflecting the face of an exquisite young woman. The woman had sparkling eyes and rosy cheeks and lovely lips that greeted the wife with a charming smile. The lips moved each time the wife spoke to her, and strange to say, the lady in the mirror had on exactly the same cloud-blue garment as her own.

The husband watched with delight as his wife gazed with fascination into the mirror. He had done exactly the same thing when he had first seen the *tagami*.

Now he explained to her that what she saw in the mirror was her own reflection. In the city, he said, everyone owned a mirror. It was only in rural areas like theirs that such a thing was a novelty.

The young wife was delighted with her gift. Who could say how often she gazed at herself in the *tagami* during the days that followed. In time, however, a strange feeling came over her that perhaps it was not

proper to regard herself so often in the mirror. After a
time she closed it up in its lovely carved box and
placed it carefully among her other valuables.

In the course of time, the couple's daughter grew
into maidenhood. She became more and more beauti-

ful, and in fact, she became the very image of her
mother. Not only her parents but everyone else was
enchanted with her grace and gaiety. Her mother
thought of the *tagami,* and in her heart she hoped her
daughter would not become vain if by chance she discovered how lovely she was. Cautiously she hid the
mirror and never spoke of it. As a result the daughter
grew up as innocently as her mother had, unaware of
her great beauty.

One morning the mother became very ill. The daughter nursed her devotedly, night and day, but still her mother did not improve. Slowly her condition worsened and her body grew thin and pale. The poor woman, continuously racked with pain, knew that the end was close. Calling her daughter she asked her to bring the carved wooden box from its hiding place. Removing the mirror, she placed it by her side. "Sweet child," she said, holding her daughter's face between her withered hands, "you must know that I am dying. Soon I shall be delivered from this dreadful suffering. I want you to promise me that when I am dead you will gaze in this glass every morning and evening. There you will see me and know that I am always with you and always watching over you."

The daughter's eyes filled with tears. Solemnly she promised her mother she would do as she asked. The mother, now reconciled to her fate, died soon afterward.

Faithfully thereafter the daughter fulfilled the promise she had made to her beloved mother. Every morning and evening she removed the mirror from its box and gazed into it for a long, long time. She saw the full, smiling face of her mother—not pale and wasted as it had been during the last days of her suffering, but instead cheerful and lovely as it was at the height of her beauty.

Each evening the daughter told the image in the mirror all that had happened during the day. She told her, too, all her cares and sorrows. In the morning she would ask her mother's blessing and guidance. She was mindful in everything she did of whether or not it

would please her mother. In all her actions she resembled her mother more and more.

One day the father noticed his daughter's curious
behavior. He questioned her about it, and the daughter
told him that she saw her mother in the mirror and that
she confided to her everything that was in her heart.
She told him of the promise she had made to her upon
her deathbed and how she had never once forgotten to
fulfill it.

The father, filled with thoughts of his beloved wife,
was touched to the heart by his daughter's sweetness
and innocence. He hesitated to tell her that the face
she saw in the mirror was in truth her own dear face.
Never could he bring himself to explain the nature of
the mirror.

The Tale of the Imprisoned
Water Princess

This typical Indian fairy tale, filled with aston-
ishing crises and clever solutions, exhibits the
marvelous and fanciful imagination of the Indian
mind.

N INDIA MANY YEARS AGO, THERE WAS ONCE
a king's son, and a son of the king's chief
minister. The two boys were the very clos-
est of friends and went everywhere and
did everything together. One day, desiring to see for-
eign lands, the young men set out on a journey. Though
both were very rich, they took no servants but went by
themselves on horseback. Their horses were the very
finest and fastest. They were white and extremely
handsome to look at. The young men rode for many
days, passing through cities, towns, and villages,
through deserts and plains, until late one afternoon
they found themselves in a deep forest. Night came on,
so they stopped by a huge tree next to a pretty pond
and climbed onto a large upper limb, believing that the
safest place to stay until morning. It was a frightening
wood filled with strange shapes and sounds, so the
friends chatted to keep their courage up.

About midnight they heard a terrible roaring and
splashing coming from the water. Suddenly an enor-

mous serpent emerged from the surface and, flinging
itself onto its back, lay floating near the edge of the
pond. The young men were astonished to see that in
the middle of its gigantic hoodlike head glittered a

marvelous diamond the size of an egg. It was so brilliant that it lit the whole pond, its bank, and all the low
foliage around it, just missing the limb where the two
young men crouched. At once they remembered that
this was the famous gem often spoken of in legends,
and that its worth was equal to the treasury of seven
kings. The serpent swam ashore, took off the jewel from
its forehead, and flung it onto the ground. Hissing and

howling, it rummaged through the wood in search of
food. Soon it discovered the horses, and, to the friends'
despair, the beast immediately swallowed them up.
Still not content, it thrashed off, roaring and bellowing,
in search of more to eat. Up in the tree the friends
shivered with fright.

When the monster had gone quite a distance, the
minister's son silently lowered himself to the ground
and went to the jewel. Swiftly he covered it with thick
mud that lay nearby. He had heard that this was the
only way of hiding its light, thereby making the
serpent helpless. Carefully he climbed back into the
tree. The serpent, noticing the loss of light, became
frantic and rushed back and forth in the forest looking
everywhere for its head-jewel. Desperately it searched
for the spot where the jewel lay but was unable to find
it. With terrible groans and cries it began to stagger
about the ground. At last it fell and, with one great
shudder, died. The young men remained for a few
minutes where they were to make sure that the creature was really not alive; then they descended and dug
up the jewel. The minister's son took it to the pool and
washed it off. When he finished, the diamond was as
brilliant as before and shed clear dazzling rays deep
down into the water. The friends leaned over and saw a
million silver fishes going by, and below that—could
they believe their eyes?—a magnificent palace!

"Let us go and see it," suggested the son of the minister. The prince agreed. They both dived in, the minister's son carrying the serpent's jewel in his hand.
Slowly they floated downward until they reached the
palace gate, which stood open. Passing inside they saw

exotic gardens and huge, well-kept grounds. Gorgeous
flowers perfumed the air, making the young men
slightly dizzy. When they reached the door, they realized that they were at a fairy palace, for the walls of
the house were made entirely of gold and decorated
everywhere with quantities of the most dazzling dia-
monds. Inside, the palace was richly furnished with
priceless rugs and beautiful paintings. Though they
wandered from room to room, they met no one. The
house seemed completely empty. At last, however, they
opened a door and found a young lady of exquisite
beauty fast asleep on a golden bed. The two friends
stared at her with rapture. Abruptly her eyes flew open
and she cried out.

"Oh, how did you come here, you unfortunate men!
Go, go, before you are killed! A mighty serpent dwells
here who has devoured the whole royal family. My
father and mother, my sisters and brothers, all are
dead. I am the only one spared. Leave before he de-
stroys you too!"

The young men calmed the princess and told her
about the death of the serpent. Then they showed her
the head-jewel and assured her that she was free. She
thanked them for saving her and begged them to stay
and live with her in the palace for awhile. The two
friends both agreed.

In a short while the son of the king fell madly in love
with the beautiful princess and asked her to become his
wife. She quickly agreed and they were soon married.
The ceremony was simple, for only the exchange of a
wreath of flowers was necessary.

The prince and princess were extremely happy, for

each was as kind and loving and gay as the other; and though the wife of the minister's son was living in the upper world, he, too, shared in his friend's happiness. Thus time passed merrily for the three young people.

At last one day the king's son decided that he must return to his own country. After much discussion, it was determined that the son of the minister should go home first to inform the royal family and the court of the prince's marriage. Then, on a specially appointed day and hour, he would return to the bank of the pond with a retinue of servants, elephants, and horses to assist the prince and princess back to the palace. The minister's son bid the king's son and his wife an affectionate goodbye and started on his journey.

Left alone, the prince and princess spent their time in much the same way as before, except for one thing: The princess began to make secret trips to the upper world.

It happened this way. One day while the prince was sleeping, his wife, suddenly overcome with curiosity about earth life, took the serpent-jewel in her hand and rose to the surface of the pond. At the bank's edge she bathed herself, washed her hair, and walked about, admiring immensely the beauty of the forest. Then she descended again to her sleeping husband. The next day, while the prince was once more napping, she made the journey again. Her success made her so confident that she repeated the trip a third time. This time, however, she was observed by two people: an old lady gathering firewood, and a Rajah's son who was out hunting and who happened to stop by the pond while his servants prepared his meal. Startled by the man and old woman, the princess instantly sank back down to the palace.

The mysterious heavenly beauty of the water princess struck the heart of the young man and he stood like a statue, gazing at the water for hours in hopes of seeing her again. When she did not reappear, the Rajah's son became mad with love and despair. Raving over and over, "Now here, now gone! Now here, now gone!" the young man refused to leave the spot until at last his servants had to carry him back to the castle by force.

The Rajah was terribly upset by his son's condition and called in all the best doctors of the kingdom. None could cure the boy of his ravings, however, and none knew what had caused them. At last the king ordered a drum beaten in all parts of the city. With it a crier announced that the Rajah would offer half of his kingdom and the hand of his beautiful daughter to anyone who could cure his son. If anyone wanted to try, he must only beat the drum to let the Rajah know. For days the drum was silent. Then the old woman touched the drum. This woman was the mother of an idiot son called Phakir Chand, and she was anxious for him to marry the Rajah's daughter. Immediately she presented herself before the ruler. Gravely the Rajah questioned her.

"You are the woman who touched the drum?"

"Yes, O great monarch of justice."

"And do you know the cause of my son's madness?"

"Yes," she said, "I do, but I will not mention it until I have cured your son."

"How can you cure my son, when the best doctors in the land have failed ?" asked the Rajah.

The old lady smiled and whispered, "Many an old woman knows secrets which the wise men do not."

"Well," asked the Rajah, "when can you perform the cure ?"

"I cannot give you an exact date," said the old lady, "but I will begin work right away."

"Do you need anything ?" asked the Rajah.

"Yes, Your Lordship. I need a hut to be built by the pond where your son first became ill. I shall live there for a few days. And I need many servants to wait out of sight in the woods. They are to come when I call."

"It shall be done. Is there anything else ?"

"Nothing else, Your Lordship, except this. You promised to give anyone who cured your son half of your kingdom and your daughter. Since I cannot marry her, I beg that my son Phakir Chand take my place."

"Agreed, agreed," said the Rajah. "Now, to work."

In a few hours the hut had been built and the old lady moved in. Out of sight in the woods, the servants settled down to wait.

The princess, frightened by her last visit, did not return to the surface for a long time. One day while her husband was sleeping she was again overcome with curiosity. Taking the jewel in her hand, she rose to the top. The princess looked carefully about, but as she saw no one she felt it was safe to go to the edge of the pond to bathe and wash her hair as she had done before. Just as she began to do her hair, the old woman came quietly out of the hut and started speaking pleasantly to her.

"Come, my beautiful lady, let me help you with your task."

At first the princess was afraid, but when she saw it was just a kind old woman, all by herself, her fear went away. As the woman helped her with her washing, she noticed the diamond.

"Here," she said, "Let me hold the jewel safely until you are finished."

As soon as she had it in her hand, she hid it inside her clothes, knowing that without it the princess could not escape. Then she signalled the waiting servants, who quickly came and made the princess a captive.

In the city there was great rejoicing. Everyone came to see the water nymph, "daughter of the immortals," as they called the princess. When the Rajah's son saw his beloved, his head instantly cleared. He stopped moaning and shouted happily, "I have found her, I have found her!" The Rajah, seeing his son healthy once again, was overcome with joy.

Everyone expected the two young people to be married right away, but the princess said that it was not possible for a full year.

"I have made a vow that during this time I shall not look at the face of any man except my husband, who is dwelling beneath the waters."

During the next months the sad princess spent her days and nights sorrowing and weeping. She bitterly regretted that she had allowed curiosity to lead her away from the happy life she had enjoyed with her beloved husband. She wanted to run away. But how could she? She was imprisoned deep within the Rajah's castle. Besides, even if she did succeed in escaping, she no longer had the serpent-jewel, and she could never return to her water palace without it. As the year drew to a close everyone in the city began to make grand preparations for the royal wedding. Rich sweetmeats, honey cakes, and all sorts of delicacies were being prepared. Fireworks were set up. Bands of musicians practiced their songs. The whole city had a holiday air about it.

All this while the son of the minister, who had returned to his country, had been making arrangements for the prince and princess. At the specially appointed day and hour, the friend stood at the bank of the pool with an enormous retinue of attendants, elephants, and horses. He was awaiting the prince and his bride to carry them back to their kingdom in proper royal style. Though he stared at the water all day long, there was no sign of the king's son, nor of his beautiful wife. The sun grew high in the sky and finally sank, but still his dearest friends did not appear.

For three days the minister's son waited by the pool, but nothing happened. At last, heartbroken, he turned away. As he traveled back, he wondered again and again what could have happened to the prince and his wife. Were they dead? Had another serpent killed them? Had they somehow lost the serpent's jewel? Or had they been captured on a visit to the upper world?

Soon he neared the outskirts of a city and stopped to dine. Festive music filled the air and the son of the minister asked why the people of the town were celebrating. He was told that a beautiful water princess captured from a nearby pond was about to be married to the Rajah's son. Immediately he understood that it

was the wife of his friend and he decided to find out
more about the situation. He dismissed his servants and
went into the center of the city. After talking with a
great number of people, he learned what had happened: how the Rajah's son had become ill, how the
old woman had cleverly captured the poor princess,
how the princess had insisted upon waiting a year to
marry, and how the king's daughter was to be given in
reward to the son of the old woman.

"A truly wonderful story," said the son of the minister to the Brahman who was recounting it.

"There is still one thing unsettled, though," said the
Brahman.

"Yes? What is that?" asked the minister's son, filled
with curiosity.

"Phakir Chand, the son of the old woman, has been
away for some time and has not yet come back. He's a
bit half-witted—you know—a little mad. He comes and
goes and no one knows when to expect him."

The minister's son grew interested.

"What does he look like?" he asked. "What does he
do when he returns home?"

"He's about your height, I'd say," said the Brahman.
"He puts a small piece of cloth around his waist, rubs
his body with ashes, takes a branch of a tree in his
hand, and, at the door of the hut where his mother
lives, he dances to the tune of *'Dhoop! Dhoop! Dhoop!'*
His mother usually says, 'Phakir, stay with me for
awhile.' And he usually says in a thick, muddled voice,
'No, I won't! No, I won't!' When he wants to say 'Yes'
he says *'Hoom'* instead."

The conversation with the Brahman helped the minister's son get a clear idea of the situation and what he must do. He immediately understood that the princess must have come to the surface of the pond alone, with the jewel in her hand, and that the mother of Phakir had hidden the jewel from her so that she could not return. In the meantime, below in the water palace, the king's son was trapped, with no way to rise to the upper world. The minister's son was filled with terrible grief. "If only I could get hold of the serpent's jewel," he thought. Then a clever idea came to him. "Perhaps if I pretended to be the old woman's son, Phakir Chand, I might be able to obtain the jewel. Then, too," he said to himself, "as Phakir Chand I might be able to get into the castle. Then I could rescue the princess."

With these thoughts in mind, the son of the minister quickly went to the outskirts of the city, changed his clothing so that he looked like the old woman's son, and then rubbed ashes over himself as Phakir Chand did. Breaking a branch from a tree to carry in his hand, he went to the door of the old woman's house. At the stoop he began dancing in a wild manner and calling out, *"Dhoop! Dhoop! Dhoop!"* The old woman, thinking her son had come home, begged him to enter. *"Hoom, hoom!"* cried out the minister's son, waving his branch and jigging continuously. "You must stay with me this time," pleaded the old lady. "No, I won't! No, I won't!" shrieked the minister's son. "But I'll show you a princess who has risen from the water." *"Hoom! Hoom!"* answered the son of the minister as he danced around violently. "Do you want to see a serpent-jewel worth the treasury of seven kings?" *"Hoom! Hoom!"* said the eager man. "Here it is," said the old

woman as she came out of her hut and placed the jewel
in the hand of her pretended son. With that the son of
the minister immediately wrapped up the diamond in a
piece of cloth and put it around his waist.

The old woman, excited by her son's return, went
straight to the Rajah and asked if her son Phakir
Chand could meet the water princess. Since the old
woman had cured the Rajah's son, she had become a
very important person in the kingdom and permission
was immediately granted.

"Of course," said the Rajah.

In that way the minister's son got into the castle to
meet the wife of his friend. At first she did not recognize him, but when they were left alone for a few minutes, he spoke to her in his own voice.

"Princess, don't you know who I am?"

The eyes of the princess grew wide with astonishment and she gasped, "Are you the son of the minister
—my husband's dearest friend?"

"Yes," he whispered.

With that she burst into tears.

"Oh, please, please rescue me from my terrible fate.
It was my own fault that I am in this sad state, but
please, please help me!"

The son of the minister quickly tried to comfort the
poor princess.

"Don't be sad. I will try this very night to take you
away."

After this he left the room and passed down the halls
and through the courtyard of the palace. Some of the
guards stopped him. He did a funny little dance and

cried out. *"Hoom! Hoom!"* and the guards laughed because they knew it was the crazy Phakir Chand.

"Let the fellow alone," said one.

"Yes, let him do what he likes," said another.

The rest of the night the minister's son kept going in and out of the palace and courtyards, getting the guards used to his comings and goings. At first they challenged him, but at last none of them paid any attention to him at all. At about three o'clock in the morning nearly all the guards were asleep. Quickly the minister's son went back to the princess and told her to climb onto his back and tie her hair around his neck. He covered her up as best he could; then with the beautiful burden on his back he went out of the palace and courtyard for the last time. None of the guards paid the least attention to him, so the princess and the son of the minister managed to escape without anyone's knowledge.

Swiftly they made their way to the bank of the pond. Then, taking the serpent-jewel in the palm of his hand, the son of the minister descended to the water palace with the lovely princess.

When the king's son saw his beautiful wife and his best friend appear again he nearly went mad with joy. They all had a wonderful reunion and talked and talked for three days, each one giving a separate account of himself. At last, restored with food and rest and happiness, the two best friends and the fair young princess rose to the upper world and returned to their own lands.

When the king and queen heard all that the son of the minister had done to rescue the prince and his wife,

they offered him their undying gratitude. The prince
and princess swore always to abide by the advice and
counsel of their dearest friend. Soon afterward the minister's son was reunited with his pretty wife, and all
four young people lived with great joy and happiness
for the rest of their lives.

The Clever Thief

Corruption among the powerful is one of the most popular of all folklore themes. In this tale from Korea a simple and resourceful old man teaches the king and his advisers a lesson they will never forget.

IN KOREA, MANY YEARS AGO, THERE ONCE lived an old thief who was known throughout the country as a very clever person —far too clever to be captured. However, one morning he was so careless and overconfident that he was caught stealing some spices from a shopkeeper. With great satisfaction the police brought the thief before an extremely severe judge who fined the old man very heavily. Unable to pay the sum, the thief had to submit instead to a very lengthy jail sentence. When he arrived at the prison he examined with great thoroughness his cell and the building itself, looking for a means of escape. Finding none, he soon gave up the idea of escape and instead decided upon another way of getting out of jail. Early one morning he called for the jailkeeper.

"Yes," the keeper inquired gruffly, "what do you want?"

"Take me before the king," demanded the thief.

"The king!" The jailkeeper threw back his head and

45

gasped with laughter. "Why should the king see *you*?"

The thief ignored the jailkeeper's scorn.

"Tell him I have a gift for him—of extraordinary value."

The jailkeeper, impressed with the old man's seriousness, finally agreed to arrange the interview.

The next afternoon the thief was taken to the royal quarters. There the king sat upon an enormous throne, looking very impressive and stern.

"Well, well, what is it? What do you have for me?" asked the king. "I don't have all day to spend on the likes of you, you know."

Before replying, the thief noted that the prime minister, the secretary of state, the general of the army, and the head jailkeeper were also present.

"Your Majesty," said the thief, "I have come here to present you with a rare and valuable gift."

Slipping his hand into his pocket, he carefully withdrew a tiny box, elegantly wrapped in gold paper with silver ribbons.

The king took the package and swiftly opened it. Examining the contents, his face suddenly flushed red with rage and his voice filled the room with a series of royal bellows.

"What is the meaning of this? How dare you bring me an ordinary plum pit!"

"True," admitted the old thief quietly, "it is a plum pit." Here he paused for emphasis. "But by no means an ordinary one."

"What do you mean by that?" stormed the king.

"He who plants this pit," stated the old man, "will reap nothing but golden plums."

A moment of astonished silence greeted this news.

Finally the king said, "Well, if that's the case, why haven't you planted it yourself?"

"For a very good reason, Your Majesty," answered the thief. "Only people who have never stolen or cheated can reap the benefit. Otherwise, the tree will bear only ordinary plums. That is why," and the old thief smiled in his most winning way, "I have brought the pit to you. Certainly, Your Majesty has never stolen anything or cheated."

"Alas," declared the king with great regret in his voice—for he was an honest man no matter what other faults he had—"I am afraid I am not the right person."

"What do you mean?" cried the others present.

But the king remained silent, remembering how he had once stolen some pennies from his mother's purse when he was a little boy.

"Well, how about the prime minister?" suggested the thief. "Perhaps he—"

But the old thief got no further with his sentence.

"Impossible!" blustered the prime minister with a very red face. He had often accepted bribes from people who wanted fine positions in the government. Surely, the pit would never work for him.

"You then, General?" asked the thief, turning to the head of the army.

"No, no," muttered the general with lowered eyes. He had become an enormously rich man by cheating his soldiers of part of their pay.

"Well then, Mr. Secretary of State?" offered the thief.

"I'm afraid not," sputtered the honorable old man, whose conscience was obviously troubling him. Like the prime minister, he had at times accepted money in return for favors.

"Then the head jailkeeper must be our man," said the thief solemnly as he turned to the last candidate.

Silently the jailkeeper shook his head and shrugged his shoulders. "I'm afraid I'm not right either," he said at last. He was remembering how he was always treating new prisoners, sending those who gave him money to the best quarters and reserving the worst cells for the poor and unfortunate.

Refusing to give up, the thief suggested several other officials. Each of the fine gentlemen, however, rejected in his turn the offer of the plum pit that would bear him golden fruit forever.

When the room was entirely still, each official trying to hide his embarrassment, the old thief suddenly burst out laughing.

"You gentlemen," he exclaimed, "you embezzle and you steal, and yet you never end up in jail!" He searched their faces earnestly, and then in a quiet voice, he added, "I have done nothing more than steal some spices, and for this I have been condemned to serve five years in jail."

For quite some time the king and his officials remained silent with shame.

At last the king stirred.

"I would suggest," he said in a low voice, looking at each of his ministers one by one, "that we all contribute to this man's fine, so that he will not go back to jail."

Immediately the necessary money was gathered and placed at the monarch's feet. Calling the old thief to him, the king gave him the money.

"Go, my good man," he said. "You are free. You have spent enough time in prison. From your experience you have instructed us wisely. Ministers and kings sometimes forget themselves. We will remember your lesson well."

And so, with nothing more than a plum pit to help him, the very clever old thief left jail a free man.

The Fox Who Pretended
to Be King

*The reputation of the fox as the sliest of all ani-
mals is a universal folklore theme. In this story
from Tibet the sly fox trips himself up by going
one step too far.*

N TIBET, A LONG TIME AGO, THERE LIVED A
very greedy fox. One day he sneaked into
a village to steal food. By accident he
missed his footing and fell into a tub of
blue dye in a dyer's shop. Hastily he crawled out and
ran away. As he trotted toward home the dye on his
coat dried and his fur shone like a beautiful sapphire.
When he got back to the forest, the other foxes were
very surprised to see such an unusual animal. Full of
wonder they asked him, "Who are you?" The very
clever fox lied, "My name is Kaboosh. I am sent here by
the Emperor of Heaven to be the king of all four-
legged animals."

Soon his words were carried far and wide by this
group of foxes to all the other foxes and to all the animals in the forest. Because of his curious color they did
not recognize what sort of animal he was, and they
agreed to hail him as their king. Immediately he began
to give orders. First of all he insisted that a big elephant be put at his disposal to carry him everywhere.

Next, he insisted that he be accompanied at all times
by a bodyguard of lions. Surrounded thus by his sub-
jects, he would inspect his kingdom.

However, this was not enough. He decreed that the
tigers, and in fact all the animals far and near, come to
his camp to pay tribute to him.

One day Kaboosh thought of his mother and wanted
her to share his good fortune. Promptly he dispatched a
fox to the valley where she lived, with a message saying, "Dear Mama: Your son has now become a king.
Come quickly!"

When the fox had delivered the message, the mother
fox asked, "How is my son doing now? Is he very arrogant?"

"Oh, yes indeed," replied the messenger. "He puts
on extremely arrogant airs! All day long he sits in court
surrounded by lions, tigers, and elephants, while we
poor foxes have no influence at all. We have to do
whatever he tells us. Often he has a terrible temper. He
curses and scowls with his whiskers bristling with rage.
'Arrogant' hardly describes him!"

His mother, not at all pleased to hear this, said,
"Such dreadful behavior! Tell him I won't come."

The returning messenger, now knowing his king's
true identity, did not wait long to inform his friends.

This news instantly enraged them all. However,
wanting to make quite sure that there was no mistake,
one of the foxes suggested a test.

"This afternoon, when the king is out for a ride, let
all of us foxes make our fox bark. If he *is* a fox, he will
answer automatically when he hears us."

They all agreed. When afternoon came, all the foxes

gathered together and raised their voices in a chorus.

At that moment the so-called king was sitting on his elephant, quite aloof. When he heard the foxes barking, he joyously answered them with a long, loud whoop.

Immediately the elephant realized who he was. "You impertinent fox," he said in disgust, "how dare you ride on my back!"

With one shrug, the elephant flung the audacious fox to the ground. Without looking back, the fox scampered off into the woods as fast as he could.

The Tale of the Oki Islands

A traditional, legendary Japanese story in which the loving and loyal daughter of a samurai overcomes great odds in order to see justice prevail.

MANY HUNDREDS OF YEARS AGO—ABOUT THE year 1320 to be exact—the Emperor Hojo Takatoki ruled Japan with absolute power. A samurai, a noble soldier by the name of Oribe Shima, accidentally displeased the ruler and was banished from the land. Oribe was sent to a wild rocky group of islands off the coast of Japan called the Oki Islands. There he led a lonely, miserable life, for he had left behind his beautiful young daughter, Tokoyo, and he missed her terribly. She, too, felt unbearably sad, and at last, unable to stand the separation any longer, decided to try to reach her father or die in the attempt. She was a brave girl and knew no fear. As a child she had loved to dive with the women whose job it was to collect oyster shells deep down under the sea. She risked her life as they did, though she was of higher birth and frailer body.

After selling all her property, Tokoyo set out for the coast and at last reached a place called Akasaki, from where on clear days the islands of Oki could be seen. She tried to persuade the fishermen of the town to take her to the islands, but no one would, for it was a long and difficult journey. Besides, no one was allowed to visit those who had been banished there.

Although discouraged, Tokoyo refused to give up. With the little money she had left, she bought some food. Then, in the dark of night, she went down to the sea, and finding a light boat, she set sail all alone for the islands. Fortune sent her a strong breeze, and the current also helped her. The following evening, chilled and half dead, she arrived at the rocky shore of one of the islands. Scrambling out of the boat, she made her way up the beach to a sheltered spot and lay down to sleep for the night. She awoke in the morning quite refreshed, and after eating the rest of her food, she decided immediately to search for her father.

On the road she met a fisherman.

"Do you know my father?" she asked. Then she told him her story.

"No," said the fisherman, "I have never heard of him." Then he cautioned her earnestly. "Take my advice and do not ask for him. Your questions may get you into trouble, and may send your father to his death."

After that, Tokoyo wandered from place to place, hoping to hear word of her father, but fearful of asking anyone about him. She managed to stay alive by begging food from kindly people she met here and there along the way.

One evening she came to a shrine which stood on a rocky ledge. After praying to Buddha to help her find her father, she lay down in a small grove near by and went to sleep. In a little while she was awakened by the sound of a girl's sobs, and a curious clapping of hands. She looked up into the bright moonlight and was startled to see a beautiful young girl of about fifteen crying bitterly. Beside her stood a priest, who clapped his hands and murmured over and over:

"Namu Amida Butsu's."

Both were dressed in white gowns. After the prayer was over, the priest led the girl to the edge of the rocks. and was about to push her into the sea when Tokoyo ran out and caught hold of her just in time to save her from falling over the cliff.

The old priest was completely astonished, but in no way cross.

"I judge from this action," he said, "that you are a stranger to this island. Otherwise you would know that this ceremony is not to my liking. Unfortunately, on this island we are cursed by an evil god called Yofune-Nushi. He lives at the bottom of the sea, and each year demands that we sacrifice one girl under fifteen years of age to his kingdom. We make this offering on June thirteenth, the Day of the Dog, between eight and nine o'clock at night. If we do not appease him, the evil god becomes angry and causes great storms at sea and many of our fishermen drown."

Tokoyo listened gravely, then spoke.

"Holy monk, let this young girl go and I will take her place. I am the sad daughter of Oribe Shima, a noble samurai who has been banished to these islands. It is in search of my father that I have come here; but he is so closely guarded, I cannot get to him, or even find out where he is. My heart is broken and I no longer wish to live. Let me sacrifice myself. All I ask is that you deliver this letter to my father if you can find him.''

After she had finished speaking, Tokoyo removed the white robe from the girl and placed it on herself. She then knelt at the shrine and prayed for courage to kill the evil god, Yofune-Nushi. Upon rising, she withdrew from her clothes a beautiful dagger that belonged to her family, and placing it between her teeth, she dived into the roaring sea and disappeared. The priest and the young girl stood at the ledge looking after Tokoyo, overcome with wonder at her courage.

Tokoyo, an excellent swimmer, headed straight downward through the clear water, which was illuminated by the moonlight. Down, down she swam, passing schools of silvery fish, until she reached the very bottom. There she found herself opposite an enormous cave which glittered with marvelous shells. Peering in, she thought she saw a man seated in the cave. She grasped her dagger, and bravely entered the cave, planning to battle and kill the evil god. When she got close, she was surprised to see that what she thought was a man was only a wooden statue of Hojo Takatoki, the emperor who had exiled her father. Angry and disappointed, she started to strike the statue, but then she changed her mind. ''What good would it do? I'd rather do good than evil,'' she thought to herself. Deciding to rescue the statue, Tokoyo undid her sash and tied the statue to herself. Then she began swimming upward.

As she came out of the cave, an enormous glowing snakelike creature covered with horrible scales and waving tiny legs swam up in front of her. Its fiery eyes convinced Tokoyo that she was face to face with the evil sea god that terrorized the island. Determined to kill the dreadful monster, Tokoyo courageously swam close and with her dagger struck out his right eye. The

evil god, surprised with pain, tried to re-enter his cave, but because he was so enormous and at that moment half-blind, he could not find his way. Swiftly taking advantage of the situation, Tokoyo struck him in the heart. With monstrous gasps and heavings the evil beast slowly died.

Tokoyo, happy to have rid the island of the dreadful god which demanded the life of a young girl each year, decided that she must raise the monster to the surface

so that the island people would know once and for all
he was dead. Struggling slowly and painfully, she at
last managed to swim to the top, bringing along also
the wooden statue of the emperor.

The priest and the girl, still lingering at the ledge,
were astonished to see Tokoyo emerge suddenly from
the water.

Rushing down to greet her, they cried out in amazement when they saw what she carried with her. Carefully they led the exhausted girl to a dry spot of beach
where she lay down.

When assistance came, everything was brought to
town—the body of the evil god, the wooden statue of
the emperor, and Tokoyo herself. Word had already
spread in the village, and the brave young girl was
given a heroine's welcome. After that there were many
ceremonies celebrating her extraordinary courage. The
lord who ruled the island informed the Emperor
Takatoki directly of what had passed.

The Emperor, who had long been suffering from an
unknown disease, suddenly found himself well again. It
was clear to him that he had been laboring under the
curse of someone to whom he had behaved unjustly—
someone who had carved his figure, cursed it, and sunk
it in the sea. Now that the statue had been raised, the
curse was over and he was well again. When he discovered that the person who had freed him from his spell
was none other than the daughter of Oribe Shima, he
immediately ordered the release of the noble samurai
from the island prison.

Tokoyo and her father, once again happily reunited,
went back to their native village, where they were

hailed and feted. Oribe Shima's lands were returned to him and he was soon as prosperous as ever.

On the islands of Oki a shrine was built to commemorate the wonderful event, and all across Japan the name of Tokoyo became forever famous.

The Farmer and His Hired Help

*How the rich farmer takes advantage of the poor
and simple peasant and is eventually outsmarted
by the latter, is a common folklore theme. This
story from Afghanistan is an exceptionally good
example.*

 NCE THERE LIVED TWO BROTHERS WHO WERE
so poor that they had barely enough to
eat. Discouraged with their lot, they sat
down together and tried to think of some
way to improve their situation. At last the older
brother decided it would be best if he went away and
tried to find work elsewhere. If he proved successful,
he would send his wages to his brother, who would
remain at home looking after the family affairs.

The very next morning the older brother set out. He
had not traveled far when he came upon a prosperous
farm. On the gatepost out front hung a large sign asking for hired help. Immediately he went to the farm
building, knocked on the door, and asked to see the
farmer.

"I understand you need some help," he said.

"Why yes," answered the farmer cordially. He
looked the boy over carefully and then said, "You look
like a strong, healthy lad. I think you'll do."

Though pleased to have found work so easily, the
boy became a bit concerned when he heard the conditions of the job.

"I will hire you as a helper," said the farmer, "only if you agree to stay until springtime when the first cuckoo calls. If you should shirk your work, however, or become ill-tempered at any time, you will have to pay me a penalty of fifty pieces of gold. On the other hand," he added, "if *I* should become angry or ill-tempered at any time, then I will pay you a thousand rubles."

"But where will I get the pieces of gold?" asked the boy. "I haven't a penny to my name."

"Oh, that doesn't matter," replied the farmer generously. "If you have no money, you will just have to work for me for seven years without receiving any wages."

The lad considered the bargain very strange. Seven years was a long, long time. Still, he needed the job desperately. "And," he reasoned, "I am a good worker. I shall just have to be extremely careful not to lose my temper. And I should be able to do that for the few months between now and spring."

Agreeing to the conditions, the boy signed the contract the farmer had drawn up.

On the following day, at the first light of dawn, the farmer awakened the new hand and led him to a broad meadow.

"Mow this meadow as long as there is light," he said.

All day long the lad mowed the field and did not return home until late in the evening. By this time he was thoroughly exhausted.

"What?" the farmer exclaimed upon seeing him, "Are you back already?"

Somewhat confused by this strange question, the

boy replied, "But the sun has been down for several hours now."

"Aha," said the farmer, amused by this reply, "apparently you have misunderstood the terms of our agreement. It is true that the sun is down," he smirked,

"but there is still plenty of light. If you'll notice," he continued, pointing to the sky, "there is a brilliantly shining moon tonight."

"This must be a joke," the lad thought to himself, and he could not restrain himself from frowning.

"You are not angry?" asked the farmer, his face contorted by a large grin.

"No, no. Not at all," replied the lad quietly. "But I am very tired and I would like to rest."

The farmer insisted, however, that the hired hand

return to the fields, claiming that otherwise he would be shirking his duty. Not wanting to break his agreement, the boy went back to his mowing and he worked all through the night. And hours later the setting moon was followed by the rising sun. By this time, the boy had reached the limit of his strength. In sheer exhaustion he dropped to the ground. As soon as the farmer arrived in the meadow and saw his sleeping farmhand, he urged him up again.

"Can't you see? The sun is up. It's a fine new day."

In his despair, the lad cried out in anger, "Curse your field and curse your bread and money! This is inhuman treatment!"

"You are cursing me," said the farmer. "No doubt you are angry."

Trapped, the boy sobbed with anguish. From where could he get the fifty gold pieces with which to buy his contract? How could he work for seven years for such a man without killing himself? Then he hit upon a solution. Signing a new contract, he promised the farmer that he would pay off his debt in installments. Dejected, hungry and haggard-looking, he took his leave and returned home to his brother.

"What has happened to you?" his brother asked when he observed the terrible state in which his brother had entered the house.

"I have been duped by a villain," he said, and he went on to explain his bitter experience with the farmer.

"It is a good lesson," replied the younger brother, "and don't be too angry. I believe *I* shall go and look for some work. And don't be too surprised if I turn up at the farm of that very same scoundrel."

The next morning he set off down the road, a mysterious smile curving around his lips. In the late afternoon he arrived at the home of the rich farmer and asked for work. The farmer agreed to take him on and offered him the same proposal he had made his older brother a few days before. However, the young man refused, saying that the offer was not big enough.

"What do you mean?" asked the farmer, somewhat surprised.

"Let us make it a hundred gold pieces or fourteen years of work without pay, if I fail to live up to the agreement."

Delighted with this arrangement, the farmer promptly produced a contract and both he and the hired hand signed it. Each seemed extremely pleased with the stipulations of the agreement.

Cordially the farmer provided the new helper with a good dinner, and then immediately sent him to bed so that he would be fresh for the morning's chores.

As soon as dawn peeped over the horizon, the farmer was up, waiting for the new hired hand to appear so that he could instruct him in his duties. As the sun grew higher and higher in the sky and the boy still did not arrive, the farmer began to get very impatient. Finally, he knocked on the boy's door.

"The morning is well started and you lie in bed dreaming away!" he cried. "Do you think the grass will mow itself?"

"Are you slightly angry?" asked the boy.

Taken aback by the quickness of the reply, the farmer said, "No, no. Of course I'm not angry. I just wanted to remind you that there is work to be done."

"Very well," answered the lad, "I shall start dressing right away." Slowly he put on his pants and shirt, and then laced his boots at a snail's pace. To the farmer standing outside the door, every minute of waiting seemed like an hour.

Anxiously he called out, "Hurry, lad, hurry! I can't wait all day."

"Are you getting angry again?" quizzed the boy.

"No, no, nothing of the kind," replied the farmer, exercising great self-control. "But we have a lot of work to do."

At last, when the sun was very high in the heavens, the lad came out of his room and went with the farmer to the meadow. Upon their arrival there, the new hand noticed that all the other workers were having their lunch.

"Is it worthwhile starting now?" he asked. "Everyone else is eating. Why don't we have our lunch, too?"

Finding it hard to refuse, the farmer agreed reluctantly. It turned out that the young boy was a very slow eater with a very hearty appetite. At last, patting his full stomach, he turned to the farmer and said, "Since there is a lot of hard work ahead of us, I think we need a nap to help gather our strength for the job." With that he lay down on the grass and fell dead asleep until evening.

Shaking his fist in frustration, the farmer cried, "It's getting dark, boy, can't you see? All the other workers have mowed their fields. Wake up! Wake up!" But the lad did not stir.

Finally the farmer shrieked, "May the one who sent you here break his neck."

Suddenly the lad rubbed his drowsy eyes and looked straight at the farmer.

"Are you angry?" he asked.

Forced to protest, the farmer replied, "No, no. I only wished to say that it is dark and time for us to go home."

Instantly the boy jumped to his feet.

"That's different," he said. "Let's go."

When the two arrived at the house, the farmer discovered that he had visitors. Turning to the lad, he ordered him to slaughter a goat for dinner.

"Which one?" asked the boy, feigning total bewilderment.

"Any you find along the path," replied the farmer with annoyance.

Without another word, the lad set out on his assignment.

A short time later all of the farmer's neighbors came running to his house in great excitement.

"What is the matter?" the farmer demanded.

"Your helper has gone crazy!" they exclaimed.

"How do you mean?"

"He has slaughtered every one of your goats! Your entire flock is destroyed!"

"*What!*" screamed the farmer, and he rushed into the yard, where he confronted the farmhand. "What have you done, you idiot?" he roared.

"Why," exclaimed the boy, wide-eyed, "I have done exactly what you have asked me to do. You told me to kill *any* sheep along the path and *all of them* were along the path. I merely followed your orders." Looking directly at the farmer, he continued innocently,

"Why, have I done anything wrong? You're not angry, are you?"

"No," replied the farmer through half-clenched teeth, "I'm not angry. It is just a pity that my flock is ruined."

At the end of the month the villainous farmer had lost all his patience. He began to plot a way that would release him from his contract without having to pay the penalty. Reflecting that spring was not too far away, he decided that he would speed up the first call of the cuckoo. Helping his wife into a tall tree, he instructed her to call out like a cuckoo as soon as she saw him and the hired hand enter the woods. Next, he invited the lad to go hunting with him. As they entered the forest, the farmer's wife caught sight of the two and she called out in a clear voice, "Coo-koo, coo-koo."

"Good heavens!" exclaimed the farmer, stopping dead in his tracks, "listen to that!"

"Coo-koo, coo-koo."

"Strange," the farmer said, acting surprised, "Spring is here already. Well, this means that our agreement is terminated. The cuckoo calls, and you're free to go."

But the boy, immediately sensing the farmer's plot, was not taken in by such wiles.

"It is unbelievable," he said, "a cuckoo's call in the middle of the winter. That's rather odd, don't you think? I believe I'll look into this."

Quietly stalking through the woods, he stopped directly in front of the tree from where the call had come, and raised his gun as if ready to fire.

"No, no," shrieked the farmer, throwing himself in front of the boy. "Don't shoot, don't shoot!"

Grinning with amusement, the boy lowered his gun.

The farmer, now completely ruined, turned on the boy and screamed, "Go away, get away from here as fast as you can! Get out of my sight! You've driven me out of my mind!"

Very quietly the boy said, "Why, I believe you're angry."

"Yes, yes! I *am* angry. I'll pay you the money. It's worth it to get rid of a scoundrel like you!"

Boiling with rage, the farmer rushed to the house and from a secret place took out a hundred pieces of gold.

"There!" he said, flinging the money at the boy. "Now go, and never come near here again."

"I won't leave until you tear up the contract as well," the boy replied with caution. The farmer did this immediately. Then the boy paid him the fifty gold coins owed by his brother, and the farmer tore up that contract as well. With that accomplished, the young man promptly took his leave, heading home with a joyous heart and richer by fifty gold coins.

The farmer, after surveying his losses, finally decided that he had learned a lesson. Never again did he trick hired hands into unfair contracts, but on the contrary he began to offer better working conditions. He noticed with surprise that a lot more work got done when his men were happy because they were well treated. Eventually, he became known in the area as a kind and just employer, and many people were eager for the chance to work for him.

The Wooden Horse

A classical fairy tale set in the magical surroundings of ancient China.

NE DAY MANY YEARS AGO IN CHINA, A CARpenter and a blacksmith got into a violent argument.

"I am more skilled than you are," boasted the carpenter.

"How can you say such a thing?" replied the blacksmith. "I am a far better craftsman than you!"

They argued on and on without reaching any conclusion. In the end they agreed to ask the king to decide the matter for them.

"What have you come for?" demanded the king when they appeared before him.

"My Lord," said the carpenter, "there is no other carpenter in the world who can make such ingenious things as I can. Yet this blacksmith claims to be a better craftsman than I." He regarded the blacksmith with scorn.

"But, Your Highness," the blacksmith immediately countered, "everyone who sees my work is full of praise. Still, the carpenter insists I am not as skilled as he."

Together they pleaded, "Your Majesty, we have come here to ask you to judge. Please tell us who is the better craftsman."

The king found himself in a quandary.

"How am I to judge such a matter?" he said at last. "I have never seen your work. Both of you go home and make something. In ten days bring it to me. Then I shall decide."

The carpenter and the blacksmith returned to their homes. Ten days later they again appeared before the king. The blacksmith presented him with an enormous wrought-iron fish.

"Of what use is that?" asked the king, puzzled.

"This fish of mine," asserted the blacksmith, "can swim in the sea even when loaded with a hundred thousand bags of grain."

The king could barely suppress his mirth. "Why this stupid fellow is doomed to failure," he mused. "So much iron, and yet he claims it can swim!" Nevertheless, he called on his men to load the iron fish with a hundred thousand bags of grain and put it in the sea.

"See if it will swim!" he called out with amusement.

Strange to say, the fish swam skillfully and swiftly. Everyone was amazed and delighted. The king praised the blacksmith lavishly. "We shall make you an official," he said. Thereupon, he appointed him Head of a Street. Pleased at the king's enthusiasm, the blacksmith looked scornfully at the carpenter's gift. The carpenter had made a rather ordinary-looking wooden horse. When the king saw it, he appeared disappointed.

"Surely, this is a toy for children," he declared. "How can you think of comparing it with the fish?"

"Indeed, Your Highness," replied the carpenter, "my little horse is far superior to the fish." Pointing to an instrument panel, he said, "Do you see these twenty-six keys? When you turn the first one, the horse will fly. Turning the second one makes the horse fly faster. When the twenty-sixth key is turned, the horse will fly faster than any bird. In fact," the carpenter stated proudly, "you can easily take a trip around the whole world on this horse."

As he talked, he aroused the curiosity of the king's youngest son. The very mention of a horse that could fly excited him enormously. "How wonderful it would be to skim through the sky and to see the world from up there," he thought. He begged his father to let him try the horse.

"Certainly not!" said the king. "How can you be sure that it really *will* fly? What if it falls down to earth?"

"Don't worry. It *cannot* fall," the carpenter hastened to assure him.

The young prince continued to plead with his father. As he was his father's favorite son, and the king had never before refused him anything, he found it hard not to give in. At last he said, "Very well, you may try. But you must ride slowly and not turn any of the keys except the first."

The young prince promised to do as the king asked. He mounted the horse and turned the first key. Immediately the horse rose in the air and climbed toward the heavens.

From on high, the prince looked down upon the mountains and rivers, the trees, cities, and people. Everything was far below him, and the higher he flew, the further they all receded. He felt tremendously exhilarated. Forgetting his promise, he quickly turned the rest of the keys. The horse responded by flying faster and faster. In no time at all, the people, the trees, and even the cities vanished from sight.

He had flown a long way when he began to feel hun-

gry. Fortunately, he saw a town directly below him. Instantly he tightened the keys. The wooden horse slowed down and landed safely. After having a good meal, he put up at an inn. He was overjoyed by his journey, for in such a short time it had brought him to a new city, one that he had never seen before.

The next day he went sightseeing in the streets. Before long he arrived at a square where he saw a crowd of people standing and gazing into the sky.

"There must be something very strange up there," thought the prince to himself. Walking across to where everyone stood, he also gazed upwards, only to find there was nothing to see.

"What are you all looking at?" he asked a man who was standing next to him.

The man looked at him closely and then explained. "The king of our country has a daughter," he said. "She is so beautiful that it is impossible to find any other girl in the world to match her. The king loves her to distraction and he won't allow anyone to set eyes on her. While she was living in his palace, he hardly knew a moment's peace. Hence, he built a palace for her in the sky. There she lives entirely alone. But every day, when his duties are finished, the king goes to see her. He has been there for some time now and he will soon come back."

All this sounded extremely strange to the prince.

"How is it possible to build a palace in the sky?" he asked.

"It was built by a god," answered the man. "Only the king can go there."

The young prince could not get this strange story out of his mind. He decided to see for himself if such a place existed. That night, he mounted his wooden horse and rode up into the sky. Exactly as the man had predicted, he soon came upon a large golden palace, nestled upon a cloud. Dismounting at the door, he walked in.

When the princess heard someone enter, she thought it must be her father. Running to greet him, she saw a stranger instead and decided that he must be a god, for no human being could possibly reach her. Cordially, she welcomed the visitor.

To the young prince, she seemed as beautiful as a goddess, and he fell in love with her at first sight.

"I should be the happiest man on earth if I could have a wife like her," thought he.

At the same time, the princess was charmed by the young and handsome prince.

"Why should my father lock me up in a place like this where I cannot see anyone?" she complained to herself. "It isn't fun! After all, I want to love someone and be loved too."

Soon they were engaged in a long and happy conversation.

At daybreak the young prince took leave of the princess and flew back to the inn. Shortly afterwards the king went to the heavenly palace to see his daughter. Now, every time the king visited the princess, he weighed her, for in his country, it was a fact that once a woman fell in love she would instantly put on weight. That day, to his great surprise, he found the princess was four ounces heavier.

The king's eyes flashed fire and his beard bristled with rage. "There is certainly some reason for this," he thought. At once he returned to his palace to discuss the matter with his ministers. "Who can visit my daughter except myself?" he asked. None of the officials could give him a satisfactory answer. At last he declared: "Let us think of a way of catching this intruder."

"We have four knights," said one of the ministers. "Your majesty could take them up into the sky and place them at the four corners of the palace. If the man tries to see the princess again, he will surely be captured.''

The king thought this an excellent idea. When night came he escorted the four knights to the heavenly palace, and assigning each his place, he told them to keep careful watch. When everything was properly arranged, he returned to earth.

Who could have guessed, however, that all the knights were such heavy sleepers that they would stand sleeping at their posts? Again, the young prince spent the night visiting the princess without being discovered. When the king returned the next morning to weigh the princess, he found that she was eight ounces heavier than before. He was speechless with anger.

Now the matter became the talk of the city. The king was so infuriated that he cancelled all royal appointments and spent all his time devising plots to capture the intruder. Then one of his ministers suggested that wet paint should be smeared upon all the princess' furniture. ''Then,'' he said, ''the next day we can search the city for the one who has paint on him. The wrong-doer will hardly be able to escape.''

The king thought it was a clever plan. When he visited his daughter the next day he painted every piece of furniture.

That evening, the young prince came to see the princess as usual. When he left, he was astonished to find paint all over his clothes. He immediately took them off and threw them away. Although his clothes were studded with jewels he did not regret losing them, for are not jewels of small consequence to one who is in love?

In the city there lived a poor old man who rose every

morning before dawn and went from house to house announcing the hour of the morning prayers. That morning while making his rounds, he saw a number of objects fall from the sky. He was amazed to find that they were clothes of the finest quality.

"It is certainly God who has sent me these," he said to himself, "probably because I have been serving him all my life." Joyfully he took the clothes home.

In the evening the whole city went to the service in the temple. Among the worshippers was a man sent by the king. The old man had happily put on his new garments, not knowing of the great misfortune that lay in store for him. Once in the temple, the old man settled down to pray, but he had no sooner bowed his head when a great hand clasped him on the shoulder and lifted him up. Instantly he was taken before the king.

"How did your clothes get marked with paint?" roared the monarch.

"Why, they were like this when I picked them up in the street," uttered the confused old man. Then he described the curious way in which he had obtained the clothes. Neither the king nor his ministers believed him. The poor man was sent to prison. After that, he was sentenced to be killed. Bound hand and foot he was taken to the public square to be hanged.

When the townspeople saw the poor old man arrive, they could hardly believe their eyes. They were sure that there must be some mistake. The prince, who had also heard the news, rushed to the square with the wooden horse under his arm.

"That man," shouted the prince, "isn't guilty. I am the one who went to the heavenly palace and visited the princess. The clothes with paint on them belong to me. If you like, you may kill me. But set the poor old man free immediately."

A messenger at once went to the king. "A young man has declared himself guilty," he said. "Tell us which one to hang."

Without hesitation the king replied, "Hang the young man who has confessed!"

The executioners released the old man and advanced toward the prince. Just at that moment, however, he jumped on his horse, turned the keys and flew off, leaving the executioners and the townspeople stupefied. When the king discovered that he had been outwitted by a mere stripling of a boy, he stamped around the castle in a terrible rage.

In the meantime, the young prince went straight to the heavenly palace of the princess and said, "Come my dear, we must leave here at once. Your father has discovered that we love one another and threatens to part us. We must go immediately to my father's palace, where we shall marry and live forever."

"I love you now and always," replied the princess, "and wherever you go, I shall go."

Quickly they hurried out of the palace and flew away upon the wooden horse. They had flown quite a distance when the princess suddenly cried out, "I have forgotten the two jewels Mother gave me when I was a child! She told me to present them to my husband's parents on my wedding day. How can I go without them?"

"We are far, far away from the heavenly palace now," replied the prince. "Do not worry about them."

"No, no! I cannot go without the jewels," exclaimed the princess. "I must bring a present to your parents."

The young prince could not refuse her wishes. He turned the keys and the horse landed. "I shall wait for you here," he said. "Take the horse, go quickly and get the jewels, and return as soon as you can."

Swiftly the princess flew away.

In the meantime, the king had ascended to the heavenly palace and was anxiously searching for his daughter. Looking out a window, he suddenly saw her returning. Quickly, he hid himself behind the bed and the moment she came into the room he jumped out and caught her. The poor princess screamed and sobbed but it was to no avail. The king took her back to his own palace and shut her in a room. The wooden horse was placed in another chamber.

Wanting to make sure that he would always be able to stay in touch with his daughter, the king decided to marry her to the son of a wealthy and great neighboring king. He wrote a letter to the king saying, "As my daughter is now of age, I am willing to marry her to your son. From now on we shall be relatives and our two countries will forever maintain friendly relations." He also proposed an early date for the wedding celebration.

While all this was taking place, the young prince remained where he was, waiting for his princess. Hour upon hour went by and still she did not arrive. Looking about, he found himself in a vast desert surrounded by high dunes. As the wind blew, the sand shifted to and fro. The sun beat down upon him and there was not a blade of grass to be seen anywhere. He was hungry and thirsty and craved water, but search as he might, he could not find a drop.

Hoping he might be able to see something from the top of one of the dunes, the prince started to climb. With each step his feet sank into the sand, and it was only after an arduous climb that he finally managed to reach the top. As he raised his head to look around, the sand beneath his feet started to slide down the dune like ice melting in spring. Steadying himself, he saw a prosperous-looking orchard before him. There were all varieties of trees laden with delicious ripe fruit, clustered thickly on the branches. Running down into the orchard, he picked and ate some peaches. They were sweet and fragrant and the juice trickled from his mouth. Suddenly feeling very tired, he leaned against a tree and fell asleep.

When he woke up and wiped his face with his hand, he found he had grown a thick beard and whiskers. He could not imagine what had happened. He had never had a beard before. He pondered over the matter for a long time until he felt hungry again. This time he did not dare to touch the peaches, for he had begun to suspect them. Instead he went to a pear tree, pulled down a branch, and picked some of the fruit. The pears were big and juicy and they had an unusually delicate peel. The more he ate, the more he liked them. When he was finally satisfied, he went to sleep again.

It was almost dark when he awoke. As he stretched himself, his head knocked against the tree trunk and it seemed heavier than usual. Feeling it gingerly, he touched two long, thick horns. He noticed that his beard had turned snow white and that it had grown a foot long. He dared not imagine what he looked like.

"When the princess comes back she won't recognize me," he exclaimed. "She won't love me any longer. Oh, whatever shall I do?"

The longer he brooded over it, the lower his spirits sank. Unable to restrain his sobs, he cried himself to exhaustion and finally fell asleep.

In his dreams he saw an old man standing before him, who touched his head and said, "Why are you so terribly sad, my son?"

The young prince poured out the tale of his misfortunes.

"Don't worry," said the old man. "Go and pick up some dried peaches and pears from under the trees and eat them. Soon your beard, your whiskers, and your horns will all drop off. Go away from here, my son. Don't stay here any longer. There are devils living here. Fortunately for you, they are all sleeping now, because if they were awake they would have devoured you."

The young prince listened in amazement. Waking from his dream, he rubbed his eyes. The moon was floating high in the sky and a cold wind was whistling across the dunes. The sand no longer felt hot. Just as the old man of his dream had told him, he gathered up a handful of dried peaches and another of dried pears, and ate them. When he had finished eating, he felt his head grow light and his face smooth. The beard, whiskers, and horns were all gone. He thought for a moment, then tore down some twigs from a willow and wove them into a basket. He filled it with peaches and pears, both dried and fresh, and hurried away from the mysterious orchard.

He wanted to go home, but he had no idea where it

was. Deciding not to worry about it, he randomly chose a direction. For miles and miles he walked through desolate sandy flats. He ate the dried peaches and pears when he was hungry; he slept on the ground when he was tired; and he resumed his travel the moment he woke up. Thus seven days and seven nights passed. All the time he had not seen even a bird, let alone a man. At last quite suddenly he found a road. With a sigh of relief he sat down by the roadside.

The first person to pass by was a man with a donkey. He told the prince that he could reach home by going east, and reach the princess' country by going west.

"What sense is there in going home after I have lost both the princess and the wooden horse?" thought the prince. Hence, he decided to head west.

On the way he was overtaken by an impressive procession of men on horseback. They were well armed and the horses were well equipped. Both the horses and the men were grandly attired.

In the middle of the cavalcade was a coach with glass windows, adorned with golden traceries, and drawn by four thoroughbred horses decked with silks and satins. The young prince stepped aside to get a better look. Unexpectedly the coach pulled up and a man came over to him to ask what he was selling.

"I have nothing to sell!" he replied.

The man pointed to the basket, saying, "Are they not peaches and pears? Our prince has been traveling all day. He is thirsty and hungry. Please sell us a little fruit."

"They are not for sale; they are my food. Have you seen so much as a single blade of grass on the road? If I sell you this fruit, what will I have to eat?"

The prince in the coach shouted at the man to be quick. Then he sent another man with a piece of gold, saying, ''Buy them and pay as much as the boy asks.''

At this point the young prince asked, ''Where are you going?''

The man pointed toward the west.

''Our prince is going to meet his bride.''

The young prince was taken aback. But hiding his emotions, he calmly asked for further details. He discovered that the prince in the coach intended to marry none other than his very own sweetheart. He accepted the gold and gave the servants two of the reddest fresh peaches and two of the biggest fresh pears. The prince in the coach was delighted with the lush fruit and he ate them as quickly as he could.

The cavalcade moved off, the coach bumping along with the prince sound asleep inside. No sooner had he waked than he began to cry aloud with fright. Quickly the ministers ran up to the coach to see what had happened. Inside, sitting where the prince had sat, was a strange animal with two horns and a face covered with whiskers and a beard. The prince had disappeared. The procession halted to wait for the boy who had sold them the fruit.

Soon the young prince did arrive. The ministers stopped him and asked what kind of fruit he had sold.

''Fresh fruit, of course,'' replied the prince. ''I picked the pears and peaches myself.''

''If that is the case, why has our prince grown a beard and horns since he ate your fruit?'' they demanded.

Far from being surprised, the young prince was only too glad to find the other prince in such a state.

"How should I know?" he replied. "As you see, I haven't grown horns and a beard and I eat this fruit every day."

The ministers remained silent, unable to answer him.

The young prince pretended to think for a while, and then, as though an idea had just dawned on him, he said, "Did your prince, by any chance, fall asleep after he had eaten the fruit?"

"Yes, indeed, he did," the ministers nodded.

"Then you can't blame anyone," replied the young prince. "You have come from another part of the world, so you wouldn't know that there is a maxim to be observed in this area—No sleep after eating. If you fall asleep, you will certainly grow a beard and horns."

On hearing this, the ministers looked at one another in fear and despair. They could only imagine that their own prince was to blame for being so greedy and slothful. But what was to be done now?

For some time they talked the matter over. It was clear that the princess would never marry their master in his present state. "It would be best if we went back at once," said one of the ministers. "We will only be driven out if we go on." But the prince felt he would rather die than return home. "I have been thinking of the princess for so long," he said. "She is mine now and I will not let her slip out of my hands."

The minister who was most intent upon serving the interests of his master finally thought up a scheme.

"Let us find a handsome young man to play the part of our prince," he suggested. "By this ruse we shall obtain the princess. Once she has returned to our country, she will be helpless."

This plan won everybody's approval. They immediately started looking about for a handsome young man. Comparing one with another, they finally came to the conclusion that none was as good-looking as the boy who had sold the fruit. Drawing the boy aside, they spoke to him about it. The young prince feigned reluctance. "It has nothing to do with me," he said. "You will have to manage yourselves. I have my own affairs to take care of."

The ministers kept pressing him to do them the favor, promising him five pieces of gold for his cooperation.

"Five isn't enough," said the young prince.

"All right, we'll give you ten," said the ministers.

So, the deal was settled. They made him sit in the coach, and they put the prince with horns on a horse, veiling his face and covering his head with a piece of cloth. They told him to hide in a room after entering the city, and on no account to let himself be seen. With these new arrangements all settled, they continued on their way.

Upon their arrival, the king came out of the city to welcome them. He was glad to see that his future son-in-law was young and handsome and that he had brought so many presents. At the same time, the king was very worried about his daughter. Because he could not predict her behavior, he had decided to speed up the wedding preparations. The wedding feast was to last four days and four nights. It was arranged that the elderly people should be provided with drinks outside the castle, whereas the young men and women would be inside so that they could amuse the prince and the princess. The king hoped that by keeping everyone busy and the festivities gay, his daughter would have no time to brood or plan an escape. Although the princess cooperated with her father and performed all her duties, she never once stopped weeping.

For three days the celebrations had been going on, but the pretty princess would not once lift her veil to look at her bridegroom. Her thoughts were entirely with the young prince she had left behind. On the fourth day, the uneasy king sent an old and trusted woman to find out whether the prince loved the princess.

That night at the banquet in the palace the young prince, sitting beside the princess, seized the opportunity when no one was watching to whisper to her that it was *he* who had come back. On hearing this, the princess lifted her veil and peeped out at him. For a moment she thought that she must be dreaming. What could her father be thinking of bringing him back to her?

The young prince, afraid that the princess might give herself away, quickly told her what had occurred and asked her to act as though nothing had happened. The princess was now extremely happy. She dried her tears, she talked and she laughed, and more than once danced with him. While dancing, they talked over their plans for running away. The young prince said that after the wedding, when she came to say goodbye to her father, she should ask for the wooden horse, and should refuse to leave without it, no matter how hard the king might try to intimidate her.

In the meantime, the old woman who had been sent

by the king to gather information, returned to him and told him what she had witnessed. "Words cannot describe how much they love each other! They have been dancing and singing together all night."

On hearing this news the king was overjoyed. He felt more confident that his plan would work.

The day after the wedding, a great number of nobles gathered at the gates of the palace to see the princess off. The prince and his entourage were already awaiting her arrival. But inside the palace the princess refused to leave. Clasping her father's hand she demanded that he first give her the wooden horse. The king flew into a rage. He even called in the executioners to frighten her off. But far from being frightened she declared that she would rather die than leave without her horse. The king was furious and at his wit's end. The nobles who were waiting outside at last grew impatient. They went in to ask about the delay.

"This useless daughter of mine is bothering us with her childish nonsense," the king stated gruffly. "She insists on taking a wooden horse she used to play with when she was a child."

At this the nobles laughed.

"Why not let her have the toy, since she is so fond of it?" they said.

The king no longer could object. Reluctantly, he brought out the wooden horse and gave it to his daughter. Then the cavalcade moved off.

For many days the procession traveled toward the east. The attendants waited upon the prince and the princess with the greatest of care. Not for a moment would they leave the two alone, thus depriving them of

any opportunity to escape. As they neared their desti-
nation, the young couple became more and more anxious. At last the young prince hit upon a ruse and he
explained it to the princess. When they reached the
gates of the palace, he told her, she should demand as a
tribute that platters of golden coins be scattered on the
ground for the peasants. If this was not done, she was
to refuse to get down from the coach.

The princess learned her role by heart, and when the
time came she imperiously demanded the coins. Eager
to please her, the officials instantly provided the coins
and had them scattered upon the ground as she di-
rected. As a result, like a swarm of bees, everyone
started scrambling for the gold. By then, the young
prince had the wooden horse ready. He helped the
princess onto it and turned the keys. The next moment
they soared into the sky, leaving an astonished crowd
gaping below. They flew toward the land of the young
prince and at last arrived there safe and sound.

The prince's father had been thinking of his son
day and night since the moment of his disappearance.
He had placed the full blame upon the carpenter and
sent him to prison. When the young prince returned,
the astounded king was overjoyed to see him. After
they embraced, the prince told the king all about the
wooden horse.

"Father," he said, "the carpenter's horse has been
invaluable. Without it I could not have toured so many
countries, nor found so lovely a bride. Neither could I
have returned to join you again. Please give the carpenter a worthy reward."

The king was filled with remorse. He told his son

that he had condemned the carpenter to prison. Immediately a messenger was sent to the jail with instructions to have the carpenter released and brought to the palace. There the king begged his forgiveness and presented him with a sum of gold—enough for him to live on comfortably for the rest of his life.

Soon thereafter, the young prince and the beautiful princess were married again—and for the rest of their lives they lived happily and ruled their people with consideration and justice.

The Khoja

Three tales about the clever and witty folk hero, the Khoja. Under different names, the Khoja appears in the folklore of Armenia, Iran, and eastern Turkey. It is likely that the ingenious Nasrdin Avanti is based on the same character.

The Khoja Teaches Tamerlane's Donkey How to Read

THE KHOJA WAS ONCE A JESTER AT THE COURT OF Tamerlane, the great Mongol warrior.

One day, a man who wanted to please Tamerlane presented the ruler with a fine, big donkey. All the courtiers at the palace said it was the most handsome donkey they had ever seen. Not to be outdone in praising Tamerlane's wonderful donkey, the Khoja declared it was surely a most intelligent animal as well.

"This donkey is so smart," said the Khoja, "I believe I can teach it to read."

Everyone in the court began to laugh and jeer at the ridiculous statement. Besides, they were all jealous of the Khoja. The great ruler commanded all to be silent.

89

"It is true that my new donkey is a magnificent beast," Tamerlane said, "but how much finer it would be if it could learn the art of reading."

It was clear to everybody that Tamerlane was very pleased with the idea of owning a reading donkey. The

Khoja, noting his enthusiasm, assured him once again that such a feat was indeed possible.

"You have aroused my interest, Khoja," said Tamerlane. "Therefore, I commission you to carry out your plan. If you succeed, you will receive a handsome reward. If you fail, you will be cruelly punished and banished from my court. Should that happen, you will wish you had learned to hold your tongue, as dumb animals do."

The envious courtiers looked smugly at the Khoja and whispered among themselves that this time he had really gone too far. But the Khoja, far from being dismayed, seemed quite confident that he could do as he had promised.

"I am not so foolish," he told the monarch, "that I would waste the time and bring down the wrath of Tamerlane by making idle boasts. All I ask is three months and just enough money to pay my expenses. After that you can judge for yourself whether I have succeeded or not."

Although Tamerlane still hinted at the awful punishments that awaited anyone who failed him, he decided to grant the Khoja's requests.

All the people at the palace expected the Khoja to work very hard during the next three months, but they were mistaken. Most of the time he spent dozing in the sun, eating, drinking, and generally enjoying himself. Twice a day he gave the donkey short lessons, but that was all. The courtiers began to whisper that the Khoja was in very serious trouble.

When the fateful day arrived, Tamerlane summoned the donkey and his "teacher" to appear before him. The Khoja walked into the palace as if he didn't have a care in the world. The donkey followed behind, looking more magnificent than ever in a beautiful polished saddle inlaid with gold.

Tamerlane and all of his court leaned forward eagerly as the Khoja led the donkey to the center of the room. In the middle was a book on a low table. The Khoja bent over and whispered something into the donkey's ear. Immediately, the animal lowered his face into the book and began turning the pages with his tongue. He appeared to be absolutely fascinated with the book. When he got halfway through, he suddenly paused at a page and began to bray. He turned to the Khoja and brayed again. Here all the lords and chieftains of the court broke into hilarious laughter, and even Tamerlane himself could not help smiling at the donkey and his sly teacher.

Bestowing many generous presents upon the Khoja he finally said, "Now, Khoja, you must tell me how you did it."

Firmly established in Tamerlane's good graces, the Khoja explained his trick.

"Between each page I put a few grains of barley. Very soon the intelligent animal understood that every time he turned a page he would find a tasty tidbit waiting for him. The hungrier he was, the faster he turned the pages. The only time he complained was when he turned a page and found no barley. Then he would bray, as he did today. I deliberately left some out. I must add," said the Khoja with a sly smile, "the reason the donkey read to fast this afternoon is that he hasn't been fed for two days."

Genuinely amused, Tamerlane said, "That's very, very funny and very clever too."

With a straight face, the Khoja declared, "I'm not so sure the donkey thinks so, My Lord."

The Khoja and the Bear

ONE DAY THE KHOJA HEARD STRANGE NOISES WHILE
he was cutting wood in the forest. When he looked
behind he saw a bear coming swiftly in his direction.
He threw down his axe and promptly climbed the
nearest tree. Fortunately, the wind was blowing
from the bear's direction, so the gigantic beast had not
yet caught the Khoja's scent. The Khoja, now halfway
up the tree and hidden under leaves, felt sure the bear
would pass by and go about his business. But the bear
did not pass by, because the tree the Khoja had
climbed was a pear tree and bears love pears.

"Oh, what a fool I am," complained the Khoja to
himself. "Why couldn't I have picked some other kind
of tree?"

After the bear had gorged himself on all the ripe
pears lying on the ground, it curled up at the foot of
the tree and went to sleep. Up in the branches the
Khoja was most uncomfortable, but he consoled himself by thinking that as soon as the bear woke up, it
would go away. The day passed slowly and finally
the moon came out. The bear, hungry again, woke up.
Looking down from his awkward perch, the Khoja
began shaking when he saw that instead of leaving, the
beast was getting ready to climb the tree in search of

more pears. Since there was no other direction in
which to go, the shivering Khoja began climbing to the
higher branches. Little by little, the bear calmly nib-
bled his way toward the top. At last the Khoja was at

the very tip of the tree and the bear was right under
him. By now, the Khoja was so scared he hardly knew
what he was doing. So, when the bear stretched out his
paw as though offering the Khoja a pear, the terrified
man shrieked, "Thank you! Thank you! But I don't eat
pears."

The poor bear, startled to see a strange man at the
top of a pear tree, lost its balance and crashed to the
ground.

By morning the Khoja realized that the bear was dead, and he climbed down from the tree. He had spent a terrible day and night and he wanted some kind of reward. He stripped the bear of its rich furry coat and later paraded through the town boasting to the people about what a very brave fellow he was.

The Khoja Pulls the Moon Out of the Well

ONE MOONLIT EVENING THE KHOJA WENT TO GET SOME water from the well. When he looked down he was startled to see the moon glowing up at him. Immediately he fastened a hook to a rope and dropped the rope down the hole. On the way down, the hook got caught on a stone. As the Khoja pulled and pulled with all his might, the hook suddenly became free and the poor Khoja fell backward with a great thump. Staring up from his new position, he saw that the moon was now in the sky.

"Well, thank heaven I'm so strong," he said. "It was a tough job, but I finally got the moon back in place."

The Poor Woman
and the Stranded Fish

This tale from Malaya deals with the classical concept of good and bad and how good and bad people are rewarded for their actions.

NCE UPON A TIME, IN THE COUNTRY OF MALAYA there lived an old woman who was so poor that she had only one very tattered dress to clothe her weak, thin body. Every day she went about searching for food. If she was lucky, sometimes she managed to obtain a very small meal, but quite often she went two or three days at a time without having anything to eat at all. Because she was so weak and small and worked so slowly, no one would hire her for the rice harvests. She was often forced to keep body and soul together by picking up bits and pieces in the bamboo forests and exchanging a tiny bundle for food.

The poor woman lived in a miserable shack which leaked badly. As she was entirely alone and had no friends or relatives to help her, she had no way of repairing it.

There was one most unusual thing about the poor woman. Although she was quite old, she had never, in all her long life, heard about the existence of God. In her country God was called Allah. She did not pray to

Him or honor Him as she knew nothing about Him. She believed that the heavens and earth had created themselves, not knowing what else to think.

One day her situation grew desperate. She had had nothing to eat for several days and was unable to find anything to trade for food. Sadly she sat in her hut.

"Oh . . . oh," lamented the poor old woman, "how cruel life is! This time I will surely die of starvation."

With painful effort she struggled to the forest looking for plants and herbs to satisfy her terrible hunger. Finding nothing there, she made her way slowly to a grassy plain overlooking a steep mountain gorge. Below she saw that the hot summer sun had nearly dried up the stream and that many fish were stranded in a small puddle, unable to swim to the sea beyond.

"What a stroke of luck!" cried the old woman joyfully. "I can eat some of the fish myself and trade the rest for some rice."

With that she started to climb down the difficult bank. As she drew nearer the puddle, she noticed that one fish was larger than all the rest. "He must be the king," she said to herself. She became quite certain of it when she heard him speak.

"Allah, O Allah!" cried the marvelous fish. "We implore you to send us rain." As he prayed, his great eyes swept the heavens.

No sooner had he spoken than an enormous downpour of rain burst from the skies, filling the stream and at once freeing the fish, who swam away toward the sea and out of the poor woman's grasp. Entirely astonished, she stared for a long time at the flowing water before she turned away and headed home. When she

was once more seated in her dismal hut, she thought
about the remarkable event she had just witnessed.

"That great king of the fishes called upon Allah to
help him. Perhaps I should do the same. Who knows?"

reflected the old woman. "It may be that at this very
moment he is waiting for my plea. Still," she thought,
"it isn't rain I should ask for. What I need most is
money."

At once she got down on her knees and raised her
eyes to heaven as she had seen the fish do.

"Allah, O Allah," she cried. "I beseech you! Please
send me some money."

When nothing happened, she cried out again. "Allah, O Allah, please help me as you helped the king of the fishes. Please send me some money."

Though still nothing happened, the poor old woman refused to give up. For the rest of the day she prayed to Allah, and for every day after that. Each morning she arose and immediately began her prayers, concerned only with them and with nothing else. She believed if she prayed often enough and long enough, Allah would at last hear her plea and answer her as he had the fish.

One of her neighbors, hearing her chant the same words over and over again every day, became absolutely furious with the old woman. One morning he stamped over angrily and shouted at her.

"Stop this nonsense at once, you silly woman!"

Astonished at the interruption, she looked up.

"Don't you know that Allah will not hear your prayers? And he most certainly will not send an old crone like you any money!"

Wagging a forefinger at her, he warned, "You would do far better, foolish hag, to look for firewood in the forest. Now stop this foolishness at once or I'll run you out of the village."

As soon as he had left, the poor old woman went right back to her praying, ignoring his threats entirely. When the neighbor heard her chants beginning again, he lost all patience and decided to play a trick on her. When it was dark, he filled a sack with cracked pottery and garbage and climbed up on the old woman's roof. As soon as she was sound asleep, he dropped the sack through a hole in the roof onto the poor woman's back. He laughed heartily to himself, thinking that when she opened the bag she would believe it was money sent from Allah. When she found Allah had sent her nothing but garbage, she would stop all that infernal praying.

Inside the hut the poor old lady was awakened by a dreadful thump. Looking about, she was astonished to find a huge bag on her bed which had apparently fallen through a hole in the roof. Scrambling to the sack, she swiftly undid it and looked inside. Suddenly a cry of joy pierced the air.

"Allah! Allah!" exclaimed the old lady. "I thank Thee! I thank Thee!" Weeping with gratitude, she flung herself on her knees and prayed. Then she arose and went over to the sack and turned it upside down. To the complete amazement of the neighbor who was spying through a hole, out of the sack spilled, not garbage, but thousands upon thousands of gold and silver coins.

"Allah, Most High," cried the old woman again. "May Your name be praised! What a great amount of money You have sent me."

In his rage and dismay the mean neighbor toppled off the roof and hurt his foot. Hobbling inside, he came to examine the extraordinary coins. Soon all the other villagers joined him, and everyone exclaimed upon the marvelous mystery of the poor old woman's new wealth. Then the neighbor told how he had originally filled the sack with garbage to teach the poor woman a lesson. Everyone was even more amazed to learn that the glittering coins had originally been transformed from a heap of garbage.

News of the miracle quickly traveled throughout the land, and the prince himself invited the old woman to recount the story to him personally.

Because of the mysterious way she had received her wealth, the old lady was now not only very rich, but also very famous. People came from miles around to meet her. She was extremely kind and gracious to all her visitors. She remembered well her own terrible days of poverty and hunger and helped all the poor and afflicted that she could. Because of this, she came to be very beloved by all.

One day her old neighbor came to see her. Greed had consumed him since the first moment he had set eyes upon the good lady's mountain of coins.

"Little mother," he said, pretending great friendliness, "you know you really owe your good fortune to me."

"How is that?" the old lady asked.

"Why, if I hadn't thrown that bag of garbage through your roof, Allah wouldn't have had anything to turn to gold. I really did you a great service."

"Why, yes—I suppose you did," said the old lady.

"So now I think it's only fair for you to return the favor."

"How do you mean?" asked the old woman, slightly surprised.

"I want you to fill a sack with broken pottery and garbage, just as I did, and throw it on me one night when I'm sleeping. Surely the contents will change to golden coins just as yours did. As a matter of fact," added the neighbor, "make that two sacks. Then I can become richer than you."

Smiling gently, the old lady agreed to the plan.

"Very well," she said. "Go home and pray just as I did, and tonight I will do as you ask."

The neighbor hurried home and prayed very earnestly, and then went to bed quite early. Meanwhile the old woman waited patiently for him to fall asleep. When she heard a regular series of snores and whistles, she knew that it was safe to proceed. Awkwardly she struggled onto the roof with the two sacks of garbage and tossed them down through a hole so that they landed upon the sleeping man's back. Abruptly he woke up and started to bellow, but then he saw the two sacks on his bed and joyfully called for his wife.

"Bring me incense! We must praise Allah. He has sent me my money!"

Eagerly he opened the bags and spilled the contents onto the floor. Out tumbled an enormous quantity of broken pottery and garbage.

"Oh . . . oh . . . oh . . . oh!" wailed the neighbor, beside himself with rage. Shaking a hand at the heavens, he shrieked, "So, you play favorites. You give your darlings money. Well, what about *me!* Or have you lost your power? Can the mighty Allah no longer turn garbage into gold?" Weeping with fury, he fell upon the floor and pounded it with his fists.

Suddenly the blasphemer was seized with a dreadful pain. While his terrified wife helped put him to bed, a servant ran out for the doctor. After the doctor came and examined the patient, he stated flatly that nothing could be done. Many more doctors were called for their opinions, but each of them said exactly the same thing. Nothing could be done. Gradually, after weeks of ill-

ness, by the grace of Allah the neighbor began to recover. He was left a permanent cripple, however, and
could no longer work. Slowly he grew poorer and
poorer. In the end he was just as poor as the old woman
had been when he tossed the sack of garbage down on
her.

The Donkey Driver and the Thief

The "fall guy" is a popular figure in folklore. In this folk tale from Arabia, a farmer is tricked by an imaginative thief.

NE DAY TWO THIEVES WALKING DOWN A deserted country road came upon a farmer slowly leading his donkey by the harness. Because the farmer looked rather simpleminded one of the thieves decided to play a trick on him.

"I am going to steal that donkey!" he declared.

"What! In broad daylight?" exclaimed the other. "How can you?"

"You'll see."

Very quietly, while the farmer jogged along half asleep, completely unaware of what was happening, the thief crept up to the donkey, disconnected the harness, and put it on his own head. Then he motioned his friend to hide the donkey in the forest.

After the animal was safely hidden, the thief suddenly stopped in his tracks. The farmer, still in a dreamy state, did not look up but merely yanked on the harness of the beast to get him going. When nothing happened, he yanked even harder. *Still* nothing happened. Furious, his eyes flew open and he turned to beat the donkey when he discovered with astonishment a man inside his animal's harness.

105

"Who . . . who . . . are you?" stammered the farmer.

"Why, I'm the donkey," replied the thief.

"But . . . but . . ."

Raising a hand, the thief attempted to calm the trembling man.

"Please," he said, "let me explain." Lifting the harness from his head, he settled himself comfortably upon a stone and begged the farmer to do the same.

"Several years ago I was human—just as you. But I became very lazy and would not do my chores. My mother grew extremely cross with me, and rightfully so. One day she discovered that along with all my other bad habits I had turned into a thief. She became so angry she put a hex on me, transforming me into a donkey for seven years. But today the curse is over and I am free to be human once again.''

Astounded by the story, the farmer reproached himself for having worked the donkey so hard.

''Please allow me to congratulate you on your freedom, and to apologize for any bad behavior on my part. If I had known . . . But what is done, is done. Here,'' offered the farmer earnestly, ''let me give you some money. It will give you a new start.''

The thief thanked the farmer, and then bade him a pleasant goodbye. A little later he rejoined the second thief, who was hiding in the woods with the donkey. He complimented his friend on his fine performance, and the two scoundrels laughed heartily for some time over the ridiculous episode. Afterward, since they had no need of him, they sold the donkey in the nearest town.

A few days later the farmer came to town to buy a new beast. While examining the animals for sale, he suddenly came across one that looked strangely familiar.

''It is . . . No! Can it be . . . ?'' Carefully studying the beast, he abruptly recognized his own brand mark burnished on its back.

''Good heavens!'' shouted the farmer. ''You scoundrel! Just a few days as a human being and you're at it again. No wonder your mother transformed you! When will you give up stealing and conniving?''

The donkey lifted its head and bared its teeth in a merry bray.

''That does it!'' the farmer exclaimed. ''You know

perfectly well you understand every word I say. Well!"
he cried, backing away in triumph, "I'll show you. This
time I won't buy you. I'll leave the likes of you to
another master."

Quite pleased with himself, the stupid farmer
walked away.

The Magic Brocade

In this tale from China, reminiscent of the great, classical Western fairy tales, magic plays an important role. The moralistic ending is typical for this kind of story.

NCE UPON A TIME, LONG, LONG AGO, THERE lived in a small village in the southern part of China a mother and her three sons. Since the poor woman was a widow, she had to support her growing family as best she could. Fortunately she was very skilled at weaving fine brocade. This material was a specialty of the Chuang area where they lived and it was made of rich fabric with designs of silver, gold, and silk woven upon it. The widow was quite famous in the surrounding countryside for her brocades, as she had a special talent for making the birds and other animals and the flowers that she wove into her cloth appear lifelike. Some people even said that her flowers and animals and birds were even *more* beautiful than real ones.

One day the widow had to go into the market place to sell some cloth she had just finished. It took her no time at all to get rid of it, for everyone was anxious to buy her work. When she had completed her business she strolled among the stalls, looking at all the interesting objects for sale. Suddenly her glance was caught by a beautiful picture and she paused. In the painting was a marvelous white house surrounded by vast fields and grand walks which led to glorious gardens bursting with fruit and flowers. Between the stately trees in the background could be glimpsed some smaller buildings, and among the fluttering leaves flew rare brightly plumed birds of all kinds. Instantly the widow fell in love with the picture and bought it. When she got home she showed it to her three sons, who also thought it was very beautiful.

"Oh," sighed the widow, "wouldn't it be wonderful if we lived in such a place!"

The two elder sons shook their heads and laughed.

"My dear mother, that's only an idle dream," said the eldest.

"Perhaps it might happen in the next world," agreed the second son, "but not in this one."

Only the youngest son comforted her.

"Why don't you weave a copy of the picture into a brocade?" he suggested. With a gentle smile on his face, he added, "That will be nearly as good as living in it."

This thought made the mother very happy. Right away she went out and bought all the colored silk yarns she needed. Then she set up her loom and began to weave the design of the painting into the brocade.

Day and night, month after month, the mother sat at her loom weaving her silks. Though her back ached and her eyes grew strained from the exacting work, still she would not stop. She worked as if possessed. Gradually the two elder sons became annoyed.

One day the eldest one said with irritation, "Mother, you weave all day but you never sell anything."

"Yes!" grumbled the second. "And we have to earn money for the rice you eat by chopping wood. We're tired of all this hard work."

The youngest son didn't want his mother to be worried. He told his brothers not to complain and promised that he would look after everything. From then on, every morning he went up the mountain by himself and chopped enough wood to take care of the whole family.

Day after day the mother continued her weaving. At night she burned pine branches to make enough light. The branches smoked so much that her eyes became sore and bloodshot. But still she would not stop.

A year passed.

Tears from the mother's eyes began to drop upon the picture. She wove the crystal liquid into a bright clear river and also into a charming little fish pond.

Another year went by.

Now the tears from the mother's eyes turned into blood and dropped like red jewels upon the cloth. Quickly she wove them into a flaming sun and into brilliant red flowers.

Hour after hour, without a moment's stop, the widow went on weaving.

Finally, at the end of the third year, her brocade was done. The mother stepped away from her work and smiled with pride and with great happiness. There it all was: the beautiful house, the breathtaking gardens filled with exotic flowers and fruit, the brilliant birds, and beyond in the vast fields sheep and cattle grazing contentedly upon the grass.

Suddenly a great wind from the west howled through the house. Catching up the rare brocade it sped through the door and disappeared over the hill. Frantically the mother chased after her beautiful treasure, only to see it blown high into the sky, far beyond her reach. It flew straight toward the east and in a twinkling it had completely vanished.

The heartbroken mother, unable to bear such a calamity, fell into a deep faint. Carefully her three sons carried her into the house and laid her upon the bed. Hours later, after sipping some ginger broth, the widow slowly came to herself.

"My son," she implored her eldest, "go to the east and find my brocade for me. It means more to me than life."

The boy nodded and quickly set out on his journey. After traveling eastward for more than a month, he came to a mountain pass where an old white-haired woman sat in front of a stone house. Beside her stood a handsome stone horse which looked as though it longed to eat the red fruit off the pretty tree that grew next to it. As the eldest boy passed by, the old lady stopped him.

"Where are you going, young man?" she asked.

"East," he said, and told her the story of the brocade.

"Ah!" she said, "the brocade your mother wove has been carried away by the fairies of the Sun Mountain because it was so beautifully made. They are going to copy it."

"But, tell me, how can I recover it?" begged the boy.

"That will be very difficult," said the old woman. "First, you have to knock out two of your front teeth and put them into the mouth of my stone horse. Then he will be able to move and to eat the red fruit hanging from this tree. When he has eaten ten pieces, then you can mount him. He will take you directly to the Sun Mountain. But first you will have to pass through the Flame Mountain which burns with a continuous fierceness.'' Here the old lady offered a warning. ''You must not utter a word of complaint, for if you do you will instantly be burned to ashes. When you have arrived at the other side, you must then cross an icy sea.'' With a grave nod she whispered, ''And if you give the slightest shudder, you will immediately sink to the bottom.''

After hearing all this, the eldest son felt his jaw and thought anxiously of the burning fire and lashing sea waves. He went white as a ghost.

The old woman looked at him and laughed.

''You won't be able to stand it, I can see,'' she said. ''Don't go. I'll give you a small iron box full of gold. Take it and live comfortably.''

She fetched the box of gold from the stone house and gave it to the boy. He took it happily and went away. On his way home he began thinking about all the money he now had. ''This gold will enable me to live very well. If I take it home, I will have to share it. Spending it all on myself will be much more fun than spending it on four people.'' He decided right then and there not to go home and turned instead to the path which led to a big city.

At home the poor mother waited two months for her eldest son to return, but he did not come back. Gradually her illness got worse. At length she sent her second son to bring the brocade back.

When the boy reached the mountain pass he came upon the old woman at the stone house, who told him the same things she had told his older brother. As he learned all that he must do in order to obtain the brocade, he became frightened and his face paled. Laughing, the woman offered him a box of gold, just as she had his brother. Greatly relieved, the boy took it and went on his way, deciding also to head for the city instead of returning home.

After waiting and waiting for the second son to return home, the widow became desperately ill. At last she turned blind from weeping. Still neither of her sons ever came back.

The youngest son, beside himself with worry, begged his mother to let him go in search of the brocade.

"*I'll* bring it back to you, Mother, I promise."

Faint with exhaustion and despair, the widow nodded weakly.

Traveling swiftly, the youngest son took only half a month to arrive at the mountain pass. There he met the old woman in front of the stone house. She told him exactly the same things that she had told his two brothers, but added, "My son, your brothers each went away with a box of gold. You may have one, too."

With steady firmness the boy refused. "I shall not let these difficulties stop me," he declared. "I am going to bring back the brocade that took my mother three years to weave."

Instantly he knocked two teeth out of his mouth and put them into the mouth of the handsome stone horse. The stone horse came alive and went to the tall green tree and ate ten pieces of red fruit hanging from its

branches. As soon as it had done this, the horse lifted
its elegant head, tossed its silver mane, and neighed.
Quickly the boy mounted its back, and together they
galloped off toward the east.

After three days and nights the young son came to
Flame Mountain. On every side fires spit forth wildly.
The boy stared for a moment at the terrifying sight,
then spurring his horse he dashed courageously up the
flaming mountain, enduring the ferocious heat without
once uttering a sound.

Once on the other side of the mountain, he came to a
vast sea. Great waves frosted with chunks of ice crashed
upon him as he made his way painfully across the freez-

ing water. Though cold and aching, he held the horse's mane tightly, persisting in his journey without allowing himself to shudder.

Emerging on the opposite shore, he saw at once the Sun Mountain. Warm light flooded the air and flowers blossomed everywhere. On top of the mountain stood a marvelous palace and from it he could hear sounds of girlish laughter and singing.

Quickly the boy tapped his horse. It reared up and flew with great speed to the door of the palace. The boy got down and entered the front hall. There he found one hundred beautiful fairies, each sitting at a loom and weaving a copy of his mother's brocade.

The fairies were all very surprised to see him. One came forth at last and spoke.

"We shall finish our weaving tonight and you may have your mother's brocade tomorrow. Will it please you to wait here for the night?"

"Yes," said the son. He sat down, prepared to wait forever if necessary for his mother's treasure. Several fairies graciously attended him, bringing delicious fruit to refresh him. Instantly all his fatigue disappeared.

When dusk fell, the fairies hung from the center of the ceiling an enormous pearl which shone so brilliantly it lit the entire room. Then, while they went on weaving, the youngest son went to sleep.

One fairy finally finished her brocade, but it was not nearly as well done as the one the widow had made. The sad fairy felt she could not part with the widow's brocade and longed to live in that beautiful human world, so she embroidered a picture of herself on the original work.

When the young son woke up just before daylight, the fairies had all gone, leaving his mother's cloth under the shining pearl. Not waiting for daybreak the boy quickly clasped it to his chest and, mounting his horse, galloped off in the waning moonlight. Bending low upon the stallion's flowing mane and clamping his mouth tightly shut, he passed again through the icy sea and up and down the flaming mountain. Soon he reached the mountain pass where the old woman stood waiting for him in front of her stone house. Smiling warmly, she greeted him.

"Young man, I see you have come back."

"Yes, old woman." After he dismounted, the woman took his teeth from the horse and put them back into his mouth. Instantly the horse turned back to stone. Then she went inside the house and returned with a pair of deerskin shoes.

"Take these," she said, "they will help you get home."

When the boy put them on he found he could move as though he had wings. In a moment he was back in his own house. He entered his mother's room and unrolled the brocade. It gleamed so brightly that the widow gasped and opened her eyes, finding her sight entirely restored. Instantly cured of all illness, she rose from her bed. Together she and her son took the precious work outside to see it in the bright light. As they unrolled it, a strange, fragrant breeze sprang up and blew upon the brocade, drawing it out longer and longer and wider and wider until at last it covered all the land in sight. Suddenly the silken threads trembled and the picture burst into life. Scarlet flowers waved in the soft wind. Animals stirred and grazed upon the tender grasses of the vast fields. Golden birds darted in and out of the handsome trees and about the grand white house that commanded the landscape. It was all exactly as the mother had woven it, except that now there was a beautiful girl in red standing by the fish pond. It was the fairy who had embroidered herself into the brocade.

The kind widow, thrilled with her good fortune, went out among her poor neighbors and asked them to come to live with her on her new land, and share the abundance of her fields and gardens.

It will not surprise you to learn that the youngest son married the beautiful fairy girl and that they lived together very happily for many, many years.

One day two beggars walked slowly down the road. They were the two elder sons of the widow, and it was clear from their appearance that they had long ago squandered all the gold they had. Astonished to see such a beautiful place, they decided to stop and beg something from the owner. But when they looked across the fields, they suddenly recognized that the people happily picnicking by the pretty stream were none other than their very own mother and brother— and a beautiful lady who must be their brother's wife. Blushing with shame, they quickly picked up their begging sticks and crept silently away.

A Very Silly Argument

Logic prevails in this amusing tale from Borneo.

 HOUSANDS OF YEARS AGO—IN PREHISTORIC times, to be exact—a very silly argument took place between different parts of the body. The Mouth, the Eyes, the Ears, the Nose, the Hands, and the Feet all claimed to be the most important part of the body. No matter how long they argued (and like some brothers and sisters, they argued for a very long time), they could not arrive at a satisfactory answer. The Eye had started the whole thing off one morning.

"I'm the most important part of the body," announced the Eye quite pompously, "because I can see what is true."

"No, *I* am," chimed in the Ear, "because I hear everything and know it before anyone else does."

"Yes, but I *smell* everything first," said the Nose.

"But my dear friends, you're all making an enormous mistake," cried the Mouth. "Don't forget, I eat everything. And where would you all be if I did not obtain the nourishment for us? That *proves* I'm the most important."

"Oh, but look," said the Hand, "How could you eat if *I* didn't feed you?"

At this point the Foot interrupted the conversation.

"But comrades, if I did not walk around to wherever we all had to go, where would you be? It's quite clear that *I'm* the most important one of us all."

Day and night the six parts of the body continued

their silly argument, hoping to wear each other out. Since they were all equally stubborn and strong-minded, they went on talking for nine straight days. At last the Heart, who had been listening quietly to the ridiculous discussion, finally got disgusted. Speaking loudly above the nonsensical din, the Heart commanded silence.

"Quiet, everyone. You Eye, you Ear, you Mouth, and Nose and Hand and Foot. You are *all* wrong." Stilling the immediate complaints, the Heart continued, "I am the most important among you. I keep all of you going. When I stop beating, you all stop as well. Only when I stir can you move. The only value of the Eye is for seeing. The Ear is only good for hearing. The Nose is only good for smelling. And you, Mouth, you are only important for eating. Only when I beat is the Foot able to move, the Hand able to accept food so that you, Mouth, can eat. Everything depends upon me. So no matter what any of you say, it is all quite clear. *I* am the most important among you."

And with that the argument came to a close.

The Enterprising Rabbit

In this unusual allegorical story from Chile, the businessman-rabbit outsmarts his unsuspecting customers.

NE AUTUMN, A VERY CLEVER RABBIT NOTICED that he had far more food than he needed after he had harvested his crops. After pondering for quite awhile, he devised a plan that would assure him a great deal of money for the additional crops.

Early one morning he topped his white furry head with a wide-brimmed straw hat and set off to visit his good friend, the beetle.

"Goodness gracious!" said the beetle as she opened the door to him. "What a lovely surprise. Come in, come in," she exclaimed while she removed her apron and straightened her wings. "Sit down," she invited. "Make yourself at home."

"I just happened to be passing by," said the rabbit as he settled himself in an armchair, "and it suddenly occurred to me that perhaps you and I might transact a little bit of business."

"Oh, indeed," said the beetle. "Business, you say. What kind of business would that be?"

"Well," said the rabbit, "it just so happens that I'm quite short of money right now and I need some cash. I thought I might relieve my circumstances by selling at a ridiculously low price a bushel of corn and a bushel of lentils which I have. One dollar and a half for each. It's a terrible sacrifice, but then I *am* rather desperate."

"Oh dear, oh dear," said the beetle, "I'm terribly sorry to hear that." She was a very gentle and sympathetic soul. After reflecting a moment, she said, "Perhaps I *can* help you out. I do need some food for the winter." In a sudden gust of decision she declared, "All right, I *will* buy your surplus. I'll come by and get it tomorrow."

"No, no," interrupted the rabbit a bit impatiently. "Not tomorrow. I won't be home. Come Friday morning at ten-thirty, and bring your cart."

He rose from his chair, exchanged friendly goodbyes with the beetle, and then went his way, after having first topped his furry white head with his wide-brimmed straw hat.

Not long afterward he knocked on the door of the red hen.

"Who's there?" called the hen from inside her house.

"It is I, neighbor rabbit," announced the rabbit cheerfully.

"Come in, come in," said the hen hospitably. "The door's open."

The rabbit entered and found the hen at the kitchen sink, preparing the evening meal. "Sit down," she said cordially, and immediately gave him a cup of tea. "Well, tell me now," she continued, "how are you?"

"As a matter of fact," began the rabbit, "that's what

I came to see you about. Things aren't going too well with me right now.''

"Oh?" said the hen with concern.

"No," sighed the rabbit. "I'm in a bit of a mess and need some ready cash, so I'm selling a bushel of corn and a bushel of lentils for only a dollar and a half each.''

"Well, that sounds like a bargain," said the hen. "I'll buy them from you if you like.''

"Splendid! Splendid!" exclaimed the rabbit. Then he got up and prepared to leave. "Come by on Friday morning at quarter of eleven—and bring your cart.''

"I surely will," said the hen. "Goodbye till then," she called as the rabbit hurried off, flipping his wide-brimmed straw hat quickly on his white furry head.

The rabbit next paid a call on the fox. After explaining about his dreadful financial condition, he then offered to sell the fox the same bushel of corn and bushel of lentils for a dollar and a half apiece.

"That is a good price," declared the fox, and quickly agreed to come at eleven o'clock the following Friday morning to collect his food.

"And don't forget to bring your cart," reminded the rabbit as he hurried off, his mind already occupied with another appointment. In his rush he very nearly forgot to cap his furry white head with the wide-brimmed straw hat.

Taking a short cut, he arrived at the home of the coyote.

"Good day," he said to the coyote, who was out making strawberry jam in front of his house.

"And to you too, neighbor rabbit," said the coyote,

not taking his eyes off the bubbling pot before him.
"What can I do for you?"

"Well..." said the rabbit. And he told him all about
the terrible money trouble he was having, and offered

him the bushel of corn and the bushel of lentils for only
a dollar and a half apiece.

"Hmmmm ..." said the coyote. "Hmmmm ..." he
said again. And then, after stirring his pot vigorously
two or three times, he replied, "All right, I'll buy them
if it will help you out."

Tremendously pleased with himself, the rabbit still
did not fail to give the proper instructions.

After the coyote agreed to come by at a quarter past eleven on Friday morning with his cart, the rabbit said goodbye. Jauntily he tipped his wide-brimmed straw hat over one side of his white furry head.

Now he set forth to pay his last call. Before long he came upon a hunter sitting on a stump cleaning his gun.

"Hello there," he said with charming friendliness to the busy hunter.

"Hello to you, Mr. Rabbit," laughed the hunter when he looked up. "How are you?"

"Well, as a matter of fact," said the rabbit, "now that you ask . . ." And in a moment he told the hunter about the corn and the lentils and his money problems. In the next moment the hunter had agreed to buy the bushels for a dollar and a half apiece, and said that he would come by on Friday morning at eleven-thirty to pick them up in his cart.

"Excellent, excellent!" said the rabbit, extremely satisfied. "I shall see you on Friday, then," he said. Then he took his leave, jamming his wide-brimmed straw hat on his white furry head.

When Friday morning finally came, the first one to arrive at the rabbit's house was the beetle. She came rather slowly, as she had to push a huge cart up the hill and it was not an easy task. As she was quite out of breath when she got to the rabbit's door, he offered her a cool drink and a swing in the hammock before they transacted any business. At last, soothed and comfortable, the beetle drew out some money from her pocket and gave it to the rabbit for the food. He thanked her graciously and was about to offer her another drink when he suddenly looked up and cried out, "Oh, dear me! Oh, good heavens, whatever shall we do now?"

"Why? What's the matter? Do tell me," said the beetle with concern.

"It's the hen. The red hen—I see her coming up the road. You must hide. Here, quickly," he urged. "Into the house, and into the oven. It's quite the safest place. She'll never find you there."

Quickly the beetle did as the rabbit suggested. After closing the oven door, the rabbit then went out to greet the hen.

"Good morning, red hen," he said cordially.

"Good morning to you, friend rabbit," replied the red hen. "See—I've got something for you!" And she held out three silver dollars to the rabbit. Happily he pocketed them and then offered her a cool drink and a swing on the hammock.

"Oh, that sounds so pleasant, I believe I will," she said.

Not too many minutes had gone by before the rabbit looked up and shrieked with horror, "Oh, dear me! Oh, no! Whatever shall we do?"

"What on earth is troubling you?" asked the hen, a bit worried.

"Just rounding the corner and coming up the hill . . . I can see him . . ."

"Who?"

"The fox!"

"Oh, no!" wailed the hen. "Now I *am* in trouble."

"It's all right," said the rabbit, thinking quickly. "We'll hide you in the oven."

In a moment they were in the house. Swiftly the

rabbit deposited the hen in the oven, where she immediately gobbled up the beetle.

In the meantime the rabbit went out to greet the fox.

"Good morning, fox. A lovely day, don't you think? More like spring than fall . . ."

Genially the two chatted and then the fox gave the rabbit his money.

"Why not have a cool drink and a swing in the hammock before you start back?" invited the rabbit. Pleased to rest a bit, the fox agreed. It wasn't long before the rabbit let out his dreadful shriek, quite disconcerting the fox.

"Are you ill?" asked the fox, concerned.

"Not that, not that!" exclaimed the rabbit. "But I just see your enemy the coyote coming up the hill."

"Good heavens!" cried the fox, "I must get out of here at once."

"Here, come with me. I'll hide you." At once the two went into the house and the fox entered the oven, where he promptly ate the hen.

Just in time the rabbit managed to be out front when the coyote arrived on his doorstep.

"How are you, today, my friend?" welcomed the rabbit. "It's truly a pleasure to see you."

Delighted by the rabbit's warmth, the coyote immediately handed over his money to him, and then the two enjoyed cool drinks at the hammock.

"You certainly have a fine place," said the coyote, enjoying his visit.

"Thank you," said the rabbit, proudly surveying his domain, "I *am* fond of it . . ."

The next moment he arose with a shriek and warned the coyote that the hunter was approaching from the bottom of the hill. Carefully the coyote suppressed a yowl, while the rabbit sneaked him into the house. An instant later he was safely inside the oven and busily gobbling up the fox.

In the meantime the rabbit went out to meet the hunter.

"Now, then, rabbit," said the hunter with little ceremony, "I've come to get my corn and lentils."

Quickly he loaded them onto his cart and paid the rabbit his money.

"May I interest you in a cold drink before leaving?" asked the rabbit politely.

"Why yes—as a matter of fact I'd like that," said the hunter.

After he had finished, the rabbit then offered him another treat.

"Won't you follow me?" he asked. "I believe I have something else that will interest you also." Then he whispered into the hunter's ear.

Immediately the hunter laughed. Then he went into the house, opened the oven door and killed the coyote.

When the hunter had left, the rabbit sat down and counted his riches. Besides being the proud owner of four new carts, he had gained fifteen dollars for one bushel of corn and one bushel of lentils.

The Greedy Farmer

*The selfish and greedy farmer is taught a lesson
he will never forget, in this ancient Manchurian
tale.*

PROSPEROUS FARMER SET OFF TO MARKET ONE
day with a wagon filled with the most
sweet and delicious pears imaginable. He
was very proud of them and expected to
receive an excellent price for his goods. Along the way
a stranger in a battered hat and ragged clothes stopped
him.

"Please won't you give me one of your pears?" he
begged.

"Certainly not," refused the farmer.

"But why?" persisted the stranger.

Annoyed, the farmer began to insult him.

"You have hundreds of pears in your wagon," declared the stranger. "I asked you for only one. That
wouldn't be much of a loss to you. Why have you become so angry?"

Quickly a crowd gathered and everyone began to discuss the problem. Most of the people thought that the
farmer should give the stranger a pear and let him go
on his way. The farmer, however, would not give in.

A shopkeeper, watching all the fuss from his door-
way, went over to the farmer, bought a pear, and
handed it to the stranger.

The man accepted it gratefully and said, "One

should not be stingy. I have beautiful pears of my own and I invite you *all* to share them with me."

Confused by his declaration, one of the townspeople asked, "If you have pears of your own, then why don't you eat them?"

"First," said the man mysteriously, "I must have a seed to plant." With that he began to eat with much enjoyment the pear that the shopkeeper had bought him.

When he had finished the pear to the core, he took a seed from it, and removing a hoe from his shoulder, dug a hole in the ground. Then he placed the seed in it and covered it carefully with dirt. After this was done he called for water to sprinkle the dirt.

A thousand eyes were fixed on the spot as the stranger dampened the ground. Soon a shoot pushed through the earth. And as everyone watched with amazement, it grew and grew and grew until it had become a full-grown tree. Swiftly it put forth branches and leaves. Then blossoms opened up, flowered, and in a twinkling fragrant, delicious pears burst from the boughs in wildest profusion.

Quickly climbing up the tree and gathering the fruit, the stranger handed the juicy, perfect pears all around to the bystanders.

When the branches were stripped the man climbed down, took out his hatchet, and chopped down the tree. Then he tossed it over his shoulders and casually walked away.

While the stranger was performing his magic, the farmer had mingled with the crowd. He watched the proceedings open-mouthed and wide-eyed, having completely forgotten about marketing his pears. After the

stranger had departed, the farmer returned to his
wagon. Crying out in anguish, he saw that his pears
were all gone. Then he realized that the very generous
stranger had been generous with *his* pears!

Upon examining the shaft of his wagon, he noticed
that it, too, was missing. So that had been the tree! The
farmer ran after the stranger in a terrible rage. At the
city gate he came upon the missing shaft, but the mysterious stranger was nowhere in sight. Bursting with
anger and with no one to take it out on, the farmer's
face grew redder and redder until he looked like a
swollen tomato. All the townspeople laughed and
laughed as the greedy farmer slunk back home,
shamed by the public lesson he had received.

The Princess Sivatra

A classical Indian fairy tale, in which hope and faith play an all-important part.

 NCE UPON A TIME, A GREAT AND POWERFUL king by the name of Ahapati ruled in Madras, a region of India. Ahapati was a just and kind monarch and the people of his land were very happy. There was just one thing that kept the king himself from being entirely satisfied with his life: he had no children. One day as he was walking through the forest thinking about how happy he would be if he just had a son, a radiant goddess, shimmering with light, appeared suddenly before him. It was the goddess Siva. She told King Ahapati that within the year he would be the father of a beautiful baby girl. Then, as mysteriously as she had appeared, Siva was gone.

Within a year the prophecy of the goddess Siva came true, and in her honor the king named his daughter Sivatra.

When Sivatra became eighteen years old, King Ahapati told his daughter to go into the sacred forest where the recluses lived and to spend some time learning about nature. Sivatra obeyed her father and went away for several weeks. Then, one day, she returned to the palace.

"Well, my dearest daughter," said the king, "what did you find in the forest?"

"My beloved father," replied Sivatra, "in the forest I talked to the blind king Yumatsena. As you know, he was exiled from his country when enemies invaded his kingdom and robbed and plundered his lands. The poor old king now lives in the forest with his son Sayavan. Oh, Father," exclaimed the girl, "I have fallen deeply in love with Sayavan and soon we shall get married."

King Ahapati was overjoyed when he heard this news. He knew Yumatsena had been a most noble monarch. For many years, in fact, Ahapati had sent many of his men into the forest to search for the exiled ruler and to bring him back to Madras as his guest. Until now the quest had been without success. Turning to his adviser Naradas, who was a fortuneteller, the king asked him what he thought of the news.

"Most noble king," replied the seer with a grave voice, "I am sorry to foretell sad events at a time when you are so joyous. But I must tell you, since you have asked, that just last night the goddess Siva appeared before me in a dream and warned that Sayavan has but one year to live."

Hearing this unfortunate prophecy, the king at once turned to Sivatra.

"My dearest daughter, you have heard the wise Naradas speak. You must choose another man. Do not plunge yourself into such unhappiness at the beginning of your life."

"My noble father," the sweet, young girl replied, "I love Sayavan. I can never love another man. I would marry Sayavan even if we were granted but one day together, or but one hour."

Bowing to her wishes, King Ahapati walked with his daughter into the heart of the forest. There, in a bower scented with the perfume of wild flowers and foliage, while brilliantly plumed birds dipped and soared above them and while all the animals of the forest— tigers, elephants, lion and deer, rabbits and tortoises— gathered below, Sivatra, dressed in a sparkling gold-brocaded sari, wed her beloved Sayavan beneath the radiant forest sun.

After her marriage Sivatra dressed modestly, wearing clothes made of soft bark from young trees. She and Sayavan led a quiet, peaceful life and were very happy together. Only sometimes at night, when everyone else was asleep, would Sivatra awaken. Then she would sit up, and with great love she would gaze for hours upon her husband's face.

But happiness shatters time and a year passed swiftly. It seemed to Sivatra that it was only yesterday that she had walked through the forest for the first time with Sayavan. It was only yesterday that they had sat beneath the great shade tree and planned their marriage. How beautiful their life had been.

"In only four days," Sivatra whispered to herself, "the year will be up. In four days Sayavan will have to die!"

Sivatra decided to move the heavens by making an offering. At once she walked to a clearing and planted her feet solidly in the soft ground. Standing very straight, she let her arms hang loosely at her sides. She had been standing there for several hours when her husband approached her from the distance.

"Dearest Sivatra," he questioned, "why do you stand
this way in the clearing?"

"I am making an offering to the gods," she replied.
"Please, dear husband, do not ask me what it is about."

"But how long do you expect to stand there?" he
asked.

"For four days and four nights," she replied softly.

"Dearest wife," Sayavan replied with great concern,
"that is an impossible task. No human being can bear
it."

Sivatra did not reply. Standing there, staring
straight ahead, she merely allowed a tender smile to

touch the curve of her lips. Dusk came. The sun descended behind the trees. The moon rose, shining gently upon the lovely girl. The wind whipped lightly at her dress. But Sivatra did not move; she did not fall asleep; she stared straight ahead, the slight smile never leaving her beautiful face.

"When the heavens accept my sacrifice and make my wish come true, then shall I move and eat, and not before," she whispered to herself.

Swiftly the last day of the year arrived. Sayavan, completely unaware that this was to be his last day on earth, went about his usual chores. On his way to the deeper part of the forest to gather fruit, flowers, and kindling wood, he passed Sivatra.

"Dearest husband," she called out in a weak voice, "don't go alone. Let me accompany you."

"My beloved wife," replied Sayavan anxiously, "you cannot come with me. You have been standing for four days and four nights without sleeping, without eating, and without drinking anything. You are far too weak from your fast. You must go home now and rest."

"No!" cried Sivatra. "I must go with you. It is my wish to be with you today."

Seeing that his wife would not change her mind, he allowed her to accompany him. Slowly, they made their way through the forest. Carefully, Sivatra managed to hide from her husband her terrible fear about him.

Because it was early morning, most of the animals were still asleep. The trees were laden with lush, ripe fruit, ready to be picked. The sun, which had just risen, was shining brilliantly upon the forest, turning the

dense foliage to a rich green-gold. It was such a perfect
day that it seemed impossible that anything bad could
happen.

After gathering all the fruit they needed, Sayavan
pointed to the river bank. "My dearest," he said, "why
don't you lie upon that carpet of moss, close by the
water. I will gather some firewood while you rest."

At first Sivatra refused to do so, but at last Sayavan
persuaded her. Settling her head against the trunk of a
mango tree, she waited peacefully while Sayavan went
a little way into the forest to chop wood. From time to
time, she heard the cheerful chopping noise of his axe
and the strains from a favorite tune he hummed. Then
suddenly she heard the thud of his axe as it dropped to
the ground, and shortly thereafter Sayavan appeared
before her, his face stricken with pain.

Crying out, Sivatra jumped up and ran to him.

"What is the matter, my husband?"

"I have a terrible headache," he replied, passing his
hand over his forehead. "I can no longer see clearly."
Dropping down upon the moss, he whispered, "Let me
lie down next to you and rest...." Instantly he was in a
deep sleep.

Sivatra knew that now the hour of death was near.
As she looked up, she saw an enormous red figure approaching her. He was dressed in a black cape and in
his hand he held a length of rope. Tenderly Sivatra
pillowed her husband's head on a silken scarf. Then
she arose and greeted the stranger.

"Who are you?" she asked. "Clearly, you are from
some other world, since you neither look nor dress as
humans do."

"I am Yama, god of the dead," called out the creature, his voice thin and hollow as if echoing from a distant mountain.

"Why are you here?" asked the young girl bravely.

"I have come to take your husband away with me." Saying this, he walked over to the sleeping Sayavan and took his life. As he strode away, Sivatra, though terrified by the strange sight, jumped in front of his path and blocked him as he tried to pass.

"Return to the village at once," thundered Yama.

But Sivatra did not move.

"I cannot," she said. "I shall follow you wherever you go—even to the end of the world."

Moved by her sacrifice and by her unwavering loyalty, Yama remained where he was. "Make a wish," he offered. "I will fulfill any wish you desire, but I cannot spare Sayavan's life."

"Restore the sight of the good king Yumatsena."

"It is already done," said Yama. "Now, leave this path."

But Sivatra stood still.

"Make a second wish," said Yama.

"Return unto Yumatsena his empire, his rightful rule."

"It is already done," said Yama. "Now leave this path. You must."

But Sivatra, though swaying with fatigue, would not step from the road. Hypnotized by the courage of the young woman, Yama did not venture forward.

"Make a third wish," he said finally.

"Give my father a son," she said.

"It shall be as you say," Yama replied.

From sheer exhaustion Sivatra collapsed to her knees. Blood drained from her face and she appeared half-dead. But still she would not yield.

"Make a fourth wish," Yama said at last.

"Give me a son," whispered Sivatra.

"So shall it be." Ordering her out of the way, he once again urged her to return home. "I beg you," he pleaded, "you must do as I say."

But as Sivatra did not reply, he waited no longer. He pushed past her down the path. Sivatra, gathering what little strength she had left, followed behind him, stumbling to keep up the best she could. Her cries of pain and sorrow filled his head and became too much even for Yama to hear. At last he halted, unable to ignore such a testament of love.

"Young woman," he said, "make any wish you want and it shall be granted to you. Never have I seen such absolute devotion on the part of any mortal being."

"Give my husband back his life," she cried.

"So shall it be." As the last word was uttered, Yama disappeared.

Swiftly Sivatra returned to where her husband lay. As she touched his head with her hand, she noticed a pale flush slowly return to his face. Soon he opened his eyes and gazed at her. Then he spoke.

"Where is the red man in the black cape who carried me away? What has happened? Have I slept the entire day?"

Sivatra gazed at her beloved's face in wonder.

"Come," said Sayavan, arising and stretching. "Let us be on our way."

Together the pair walked home slowly, bathed in the silver light of the new moon.

When they arrived at the village, they found everyone greatly excited. A miraculous event had occurred. Good King Yumatsena had suddenly regained his sight. Unbearably happy, he gazed upon his son and upon his daughter-in-law for the first time.

But there was little time for everyone to accustom himself to this event before another miracle occurred. Messengers on horseback speeded through the forest to inform the old monarch of his reclaimed kingdom.

"Your enemy is dead, my lord. There has been an uprising and the cruel one has been slain by his own soldiers. Your people await your return."

Bewildered by all his good fortune, the king turned to the young couple for some kind of explanation.

"What is happening," he exclaimed, "I feel surrounded by miracles!"

Now Sivatra stepped forward, and for the first time recounted the prophecy about Sayavan's fate. Then she told about her sacrifice and finally about her meeting with Yama, the god of the dead. And she told all that had passed between them.

"Everything is happening as it is supposed to," she said quietly, "and those events that have not yet come to pass will take place." Looking about, she added softly, "Faith heals everything. It is something we have learned and must remember for the rest of our lives."

The Elephant Makes the Tiger
A Dangerous Wager

*A comical folk tale from Papua in which two
animals make the kind of bet that two good
friends should never make.*

ANY YEARS AGO WHEN JAVA WAS A VERY
young country, the animal kingdom was
in charge of running things. At this time
all the beasts were friends with each other
and no two were closer than Lightning, the tiger, and
Bongo, the elephant. One day the two best friends
went out for a walk in the jungle and came upon Lulu,
the baboon, making a terrible racket in the trees.

"Such a noisy creature," said the tiger.

"So crude and ill-mannered," added the elephant.

"I wish we could do something about it."

"Perhaps we can," said Bongo after a sudden in-
spiration. "I'll tell you what, Lightning, I'll make you a
wager."

"What kind of wager?" asked the tiger skeptically.

"If I succeed in scaring Mr. Lulu so that he falls
down out of his tree, I'll eat you. If I fail, but you
succeed, then you can eat me." Bongo waited while his
friend thought it over, then he asked, "Well, what
about it? Do you agree?"

Lightning nodded his head briskly.

142

"Why yes, Bongo, I do. It's a fine bet." Ready to begin at once, he said, "All right. You go first."

Bongo approached the tree and grasped it firmly with his trunk. Then he shook and shook and shook as hard as he possibly could. Up in the tip-top branches, Mr. Lulu barely managed to hang on as he was swung this way and that in wild arcs. Then Bongo stopped shaking the tree and began to bellow at the top of his voice. The terrible sound filled the forest and echoed in the great mountains beyond. Poor Mr. Lulu was very nearly paralyzed with fright, but somehow managed to gather his strength and leap from the branches to a tree farther away without once losing his footing. Utterly exhausted from his efforts, Bongo sat down panting and told Lightning to take his turn.

Purposefully the tiger approached Mr. Lulu's new hiding place and crouched before it. Then he started to make faces so fearful that even Bongo, who was three times his size, began to cower and hide his eyes. First Lightning showed his horrible huge fangs. Then his entire mouth. Mr. Lulu could see way down to his tonsils and then beyond. Hypnotized by the terrible hole, the poor baboon loosened his grip. When the tiger suddenly roared and rushed at him, he was already so weak with terror that he immediately came tumbling out of the tree onto the ground before them.

"Well, my friend," said Lightning, turning to Bongo, "now I guess I can eat you."

Mr. Lulu, who was quite bewildered at this turn of

events, quickly scampered away while he had the chance.

"Yes," Bongo bravely replied, "you won the bet fairly." Reluctant to surrender himself to the ordeal, he

asked the tiger for a reprieve. "Let me have seven days so that I may go home and say goodbye to my family for the last time."

"All right," agreed the tiger kindly. "But I'll expect you back on the seventh day."

Moaning and groaning at his terrible fate, Bongo staggered home through the jungle. When his wife saw him in such a dreadful state, she could not imagine what had happened.

"My poor husband, what is the matter? Are you hurt? Did you have an accident?"

"No, no," sobbed Bongo, "nothing so simple as that." Then he explained about the silly bet he had made with his friend the tiger, and the awful consequences of the affair.

For the next week Bongo sat in the corner weeping and wailing, entirely unable to eat or sleep. As the days passed and the end of the week grew closer, Bongo's sobs grew louder and louder until they nearly deafened the inhabitants of the forest. At last his friend the deer, upset by the awful clamor, came over to inquire what the matter was.

"Are you ill, poor Bongo? Whatever is the cause for all these sad sounds I've been hearing?"

"Oh, friend deer," said Bongo, "I have every good reason to sound so sad. If you only knew what trouble I'm in!" And immediately he began to tell his friend about the bet. When he had finished, the deer sat quietly for some moments, reflecting upon the situation.

"If the tiger had eaten you," he said at last, "I would be terribly sad. As things stand, I am neither one thing nor the other. I am simply amazed at the stupidity of such a wager!"

"If you would only help me out," pleaded Bongo, "I and all my children will be in your debt forever. We shall always be there to aid you when you need us."

"All right," decided the deer. "I will help you. First, you must go and find a jug full of palm-tree syrup."

Wasting no time, Bongo raced to the house of a native who was famous for his palm-tree syrup. When he returned with a huge pot of it, the deer instructed him to pour it all over his back and to make sure that it ran down his flanks and along his legs.

"Now," explained the deer, "when I begin to lick the syrup from your body, trumpet very loudly and stagger back and forth so everyone will think that I have wounded you very badly."

Together the two friends set off and traveled through the forest at high speed. Whenever they met anyone, the elephant would let out the most heartrending cries and stagger back and forth in pain, while the deer would smack his lips and look quite wild. At last they met Lightning. Immediately Bongo started weaving about and then toppled dramatically upon the ground, roaring all the while in agony. Jabbing at him with his horns and tongue, the deer shouted out, "An elephant like this is easily taken care of! If I could only grab this big, fat old tiger, then I might really satisfy my hunger!"

When Lightning heard this, he became very scared and ran away as fast as his legs could carry him. Soon he met a chimpanzee.

"Why are you running so fast?" inquired the chimp. "What's all the roaring about? And why these tremendous leaps?"

"Oh, my dear friend," Lightning gasped, "some horrible monster is sitting on Bongo's back and eating huge chunks of him. Poor Bongo is staggering about shouting and sobbing with the most terrible pain. And to make matters worse," said the tiger, his teeth chattering frantically, "the monster shrieked that if he could only catch *me* his hunger would be satisfied!"

"Friend tiger," grinned the monkey with amusement, "just what kind of monster was it crouching on the elephant's back?"

"I have no idea," replied Lightning, "but he must be terribly fierce."

The chimpanzee thought a minute and said, "It wouldn't surprise me if it wasn't our friend the deer, playing some kind of trick."

"That's impossible," said the tiger flatly. "That little deer could never eat me! Besides, he's a vegetarian."

"Well, come on," said the chimp, "let's go have a look."

When the deer, who was still sitting on Bongo's back, saw the chimp and the tiger approaching, he shouted, "Hello there, Cousin Chimp! You're a fine friend! First you promise to bring two tigers for my meal and now you arrive with only this old beast. He looks indigestible. I don't think I'll bother with him!"

When Lightning heard this he backed up, then turned and fled through the forest, roaring with fright. After the chimpanzee finally managed to catch up to him, the tiger shook a paw at him and said angrily, "That was a dirty trick you played on me, Cousin Chimp. It was a very lucky thing that the monster didn't like my looks. I'm warning you . . . the next time I run across you, I'm going to eat you."

When the poor chimpanzee tried to explain what had really happened, the tiger wasn't the least bit interested.

And that undoubtedly is the reason that from that day to this, tigers and monkeys are still not friends.

Who Is the Most Sensitive?

In this tall tale from Pakistan, some people's extreme sensitivity is given humorous expression.

HERE WERE ONCE A GREEK, A SYRIAN, AND three Pakistanis sitting around a table. Each one described to the others how extremely sensitive he was.

"Yesterday I observed a farmer plow his fields," stated the Syrian. "Merely by watching him I got a rupture."

At this the Greek shouted, "Stop! Stop! Just listening to you gives me a terrible stitch in my side."

The first Pakistani began to laugh.

"You call that sensitive? Why I'm so sensitive that one day when I ate a marvelous rice dish I could clearly taste fish. I finally discovered that five miles from the paddy where the rice was picked a fisherman's wife had buried a sardine scale."

The second Pakistani waved the story away with a flourish.

"That's nothing. Once I met a beautiful girl who always smelled to me like a goat. When I finally asked her about it, she said that when she was two years old she had once drunk a glass of goat's milk."

The third Pakistani conceded that these were all very impressive examples of sensitivity.

"Still, compared to me, you are all as hard as nails," he said.

"How is that?" demanded the others.

"Last night, for example," he began, "I went to bed on ten mattresses and I still couldn't get a wink of sleep. I finally found a grain of rice stuck in a bed-spring. Now my back is full of welts."

For a few moments there was silence. Then the Syrian started again.

"I don't think that any of us is as sensitive as a queen I once met. She told me that she was badly injured one day when a lotus blossom fell on her lap."

"Wasn't it her daughter," injected the Greek, "who was burned by the rays of the moon?"

"Possibly," said the first Pakistani, "yet in spite of it, she doesn't compare to the princess who broke out in boils whenever she heard a bird sing. If you ask me, *she* was the most sensitive."

After a prolonged discussion, the five friends decided unanimously that a princess too delicate to hear a bird's serenade should indeed be crowned the most sensitive one of all.

Tales of Nasrdin Avanti

Seven humorous and witty tales about the simple Asiatic folk hero Nasrdin Avanti, who at all times has a pertinent and ready answer for anyone who tries to outsmart him.

The Pot Bears a Son

ONE DAY NASRDIN AVANTI BORROWED A BIG IRON POT from a rich neighbor who was known to be very stingy. The villagers were surprised at the rich man's sudden generosity until they discovered that he hadn't lent the pot to Avanti but *rented* it.

After some time had elapsed Avanti paid a call on his creditor.

"Congratulations!" he shouted heartily. "Congratulations to you!"

"What for?" asked the man, surprised.

"Why, your big pot has just given birth to a little son," declared Avanti.

"Nonsense!" snorted the neighbor. "How can a pot give birth to a son?"

"Well, if you don't believe me," replied Avanti in an offended tone, "how do you explain this?"

151

Carefully he undid a package and held up a small iron pot.

"Good grief!" said the rich man to himself, "If Avanti is such a silly fool, why shouldn't I take advan-

tage of him?" Immediately he pretended to be delighted about the pot's new son, and agreed with Nasrdin that the little fellow was truly a splendid-looking creature.

Nasrdin then placed the pot in the rich man's hands and exclaimed once more, "What a handsome son!" After that he took his leave.

As he was on his way out the door, the rich man called after him, "Take good care of the big pot—and may it have many more little sons like this one!"

After several weeks Avanti paid another call upon his neighbor. This time his face was very sad.

Mournfully he said, "I have come to express my sorrow to you." Then he began to weep.

"What on earth has happened?" cried the man, upset.

"Your big pot is dead," announced Avanti.

"*What!*" shrieked the neighbor. "Impossible! How can a pot die?"

Abruptly Avanti's tears stopped flowing and he quickly said, "If the big pot can give birth to a son, why can't it die?"

Suddenly the rich man realized Avanti had played a trick on him. Not wanting to lose the pot, he shrewdly retorted, "Well, since the big pot is dead, would you please send its corpse back to me?"

"I'm sorry," said Avanti. "I buried it."

"Where?" demanded the creditor.

"In the blacksmith's forge," said Avanti smugly.

Now the rich man knew he was completely outwitted. "You swindler!" he screamed. "You thief!" he shouted. "You just want to rob me of my pot!"

"You robbed me of my small pot first," accused Avanti.

Now the two started a loud quarrel, which was exactly what Avanti wished for. Soon all the villagers came running to ask what the trouble was. When Avanti told them, they all turned to the rich man and laughed and laughed at him until he retired, thoroughly humiliated.

Two Difficult Questions

THERE WERE ONCE TWO NOBLES WHO VISITED A NEIGH-
boring kingdom and were entertained lavishly by the
monarch of the land. Deciding to test the intelligence
of the king and his court, they asked if anyone could
answer two difficult questions. The king gathered about
him his ministers and magicians, his orators and coun-
sellors, but not one of them was able to answer the
questions of the two nobles. Humiliated by such a failure, the king growled, "Is there not a single wise man in
my kingdom?"

"Yes, Your Highness," said one man, kneeling before
the ruler. "There is. A man by the name of Nasrdin
Avanti."

"Summon him immediately!" ordered the monarch.

Soon Avanti appeared before the court and was
asked the first question.

"The earth has a navel," declared one of the nobles.
"Where is it?"

Without hesitating, Avanti pointed his stick.

"Right there, on that piece of ground under the
King's left foot."

"What!" said the noble with astonishment. "How do
you know that?"

"Well," said Avanti with a triumphant grin, "if you
don't believe me, measure it yourself!"

The noble, outwitted by Avanti's reply, had nothing
more to say.

His friend stood up and quickly asked the second question.

"How many stars are in the sky?"

"Why that's simple," declared Avanti. "Exactly the same number as there are hairs on my donkey's back."

"Why that's impossible!" snorted the noble. "How can you count the hairs on a donkey's back?"

"Exactly!" said Avanti with amusement. "And how can you count the stars in the sky?"

The Ring

AVANTI HAD A BUSINESS FRIEND WHO WAS GOING AWAY on a long journey. When he came to say goodbye, he noticed that Avanti was wearing a handsome gold ring and schemed to get it.

"Avanti," he declared. "I shall miss you very much when I'm away. Why not give me your ring, and whenever I look at it, I'll think of you?"

The gold ring was the only valuable thing that Avanti had ever owned in his life and he did not want to give it up.

Solemnly he replied, "Your affection has touched me deeply. I shall miss you, too. But perhaps it's better if *I* keep the ring. Then, whenever I look at it, I will recall how you asked me for it and I didn't give it to you. That way I shall think of you always."

The Sun or the Moon

ONCE NASRDIN AVANTI WAS ASKED BY A FRIEND, "WHICH is better, the moon or the sun?"

"Why the moon, of course," replied Avanti.

"What makes you say that?" asked the friend.

"It's perfectly obvious," declared Avanti. "Look, the sun comes out during the day, but what difference does it make? It's always bright then, anyway. On the other hand, if it weren't for the moon, it would be pitch dark all night."

The Silly Tradesman

A SILLY TRADESMAN ASKED AVANTI, "WHAT WILL HAP-pen to all the fish in the ocean if the water is set on fire?"

"They'll climb a tree, of course," replied Avanti.

The Old Moon

ONE DAY A CHILD ASKED AVANTI, "WHAT BECOMES OF the old moon when the new moon comes up?"

"After the new moon comes up," said Avanti, "God cuts the old moon into little pieces and makes stars."

Good Advice

ONCE, AVANTI NEEDED SOME EXTRA MONEY. HE DECIDED
to earn it by working as a porter. In the market place
a man came around looking for someone to carry a
huge crate of dishes for him, saying:

"Whoever takes this home for me shall earn three
pieces of good advice for his pay."

Now all the other porters immediately refused the
man's terms, but Avanti, who was always willing to
learn something, decided to take the job.

On the way home Avanti asked for the first piece of
advice.

"Don't believe anybody who tells you that it's better
to go hungry than eat your fill," said the man.

"That's very good advice," agreed Avanti.

After a little while had gone by he asked for the
second piece.

"Don't believe anybody who tells you that it's better
to walk than ride horseback."

"Excellent!" exclaimed Avanti. "Really excellent
advice."

Proceeding further, Avanti asked for the third piece
of advice.

"Don't believe anyone who tells you there exists a
porter more stupid than you," laughed the man.

But no sooner had he finished speaking than Avanti dropped his crate.

"And don't believe anyone who tells you your dishes aren't broken," he roared.

The Garden of the Virtuous Queen

This classic fairy tale from Turkestan, relating the exploits of the brave and heroic youngest son of a legendary king, is a great favorite throughout the Near East.

NCE UPON A TIME THERE LIVED A WISE BUT exacting king who had three sons. One day the king was stricken with an illness which also affected his sight. His sons, sad to see their father blind and in such broken health, determined to do something about it.

"Father," they said, "we want to make you well again. Is there a remedy anywhere in the world that will restore you? If there is, command us to find it and we will do so even at the cost of our lives."

The king, touched by his sons' concern replied, "There is such a remedy, but I fear that it is far too difficult for you to obtain."

"Let us be the judge of that, good father," answered the sons. "Let us test ourselves and find out."

"The medicine I need can only be obtained from the garden of the virtuous queen. It is the fruit that grows abundantly inside her palace walls. That, and that alone, is the only cure for my illness."

After some discussion, the eldest son was chosen to set off on the mission of the king's medicine. Armed with a silver lance and a shield embossed with the

royal coat of arms, he sped away upon a prancing
white steed. He rode over the vast mountains of his
father's kingdom and to strange lands beyond. He
crossed Craggy Mountain, Tumbledown Mountain, the
Mountain of Snow, and the Mountain of Ice.

As he descended the Mountain of Ice he met an old
man with a long beard as white as snow. The man was
mending cracks in the road.

"Greetings to you, old man!" laughed the eldest son.
Jestingly he added, "May your labors come to naught!"

"Greetings to you, my son," answered the old man,
"and may your work also fail."

The young man rode on until he came at last to a
green country where the streams flowed with milk
while the peaches ripened in the winter. In a lush garden he saw a tree laden with juicy fruit. "This must be
the garden of the virtuous queen," said the son to himself. Immediately he filled his sack full of fruit and rode
home at great speed.

After arriving at the palace, he went straight to the
king.

"I greet you, Father," he said, kneeling before him.

"I greet you too, my son," replied the king, "but why
have you tarried so long?"

"See, Father," said the boy, handing the sack of fruit
to him, "I have brought your medicine from the land
where the streams flow with milk and peaches ripen in
the winter."

"Alas," said the king with deep disappointment, "I
know that land well, but it is far from the garden of the
virtuous queen. I went often to that place when I was a

youth. It took me no longer to get there than it takes to bake a pie.''

Embarrassed by his mistake, the eldest son retired. The second son now begged permission to try to obtain the medicine. When it was granted, he set out at high speed, handsomely armed, and mounted on a golden mare.

Beyond the Mountain of Ice he came across the old man with the long white beard patching the road.

''I greet you old man,'' he called out, chuckling. ''May your work fail.''

''And greetings to you in return, my son,'' answered the old man. ''May your work fail, also.''

Riding on, the second son passed through the land where streams flowed with milk and peaches ripened in winter. He crossed a flat desolate area where a river bubbled with tar and dust lay like a thick carpet upon the ground. Beyond that he saw a garden of indescribable beauty. Surely, if paradise existed, it was here. Delicious fruit and marvelous flowers abounded in great profusion. Perfume filled the air and the sun shone gently down upon the perfect land.

''This is obviously the garden of the virtuous queen,'' the second son said to himself. Quickly filling his saddlebags with fruit, he reined his horse about and headed home.

After arriving at the palace, he went straight to the king.

''Father, I greet you,'' he said, kneeling first, then handing the sack of precious fruit to the king.

''And I greet you too, my son!'' replied his father Restraining the boy with a light hand, he continued,

"Why do you return so late, and why do you appear to be in such haste?"

"Father," said the son, "I rode through the land where the streams flow with milk and the peaches ripen in winter, and then beyond to a desolate region where the river bubbles with tar and dust lies like a thick carpet on the ground. A little way from there I found a garden that was clearly a paradise, and I was most certain that this must be the garden of the virtuous queen. Quickly I plucked the delicious fruit that abounded everywhere and brought it home to you. But now I must confess, I am most anxious to get back to this wonderful place."

"Alas," said the king, sadder than ever. "When I was young I rode to that country in less time than it takes to build a fire. It is still a very great distance from the true garden of the virtuous queen." Sighing, his head fell upon his breast.

Now the youngest son was more determined than ever that his father should obtain the proper medicine. He declared that this time he was going on the quest.

Without bothering about lances and arms, he set off on his silken black horse and rode till he crossed Craggy Mountain, Tumbledown Mountain, the Mountain of Snow, and the Mountain of Ice. As he descended the Mountain of Ice he came upon the old man with the long white beard mending the road.

"Greetings to you, little father! May your work prosper," he said.

"Greetings to you in return, my son!" answered the old man. "May your work also succeed."

"I wonder, could you give me a piece of advice?"

asked the boy politely. "I wish to find the garden of the virtuous queen, so that I might gather fruit there."

"Certainly," replied the old man. "But I will give you more than one piece of advice, my son. I will give you three. Now listen carefully. First you will come to a stream frothing with milk, then one bubbling with oil, and finally one flowing with honey. At that stream you will be as far from the garden of the virtuous queen as you will be from here. Further on you will come upon three ornate towers that climb to heaven. One is of crystal, the other is of silver, and the third is made of gold. These are the towers in which the virtuous queen lives. Outside the castle walls you will discover an iron lock.

"Do not for a moment think that you can open it with your hands," warned the old man. "You must first drive a nail into a stick, and with that tool you can then open the lock. When you enter the garden, there is a second precaution. You must wrap your feet in grass. Near the castle stand several trees with the fruit you desire, but you must not pick them without first splitting a stick and using that to detach the fruit from the boughs."

After gratefully thanking the old man for his advice, the young man mounted his steed and spurred it toward the land of the virtuous queen. After crossing the stream flowing with milk, the stream flowing with oil, and the stream flowing with honey, the youth at last sighted in the distance three splendid towers of crystal, silver, and gold. Drawing close to the outside walls, he halted and tied his horse. Finding a stick, he drove a nail into it and at once thrust it into the iron lock.

Crying out, the lock complained, "Help, help, we are being forced by iron."

"Who could force iron but iron," murmured the virtuous queen from the recesses of her tower. "Do be quiet and let me sleep."

The queen believed that perhaps the lock was rusty and one part of it was merely pressing against another.

Wrapping his feet in grass, the youth now stepped inside the garden.

"Help, help," cried out the grass. "We are being assaulted by grass."

"Naturally," whispered the queen with annoyance. "What else could press against grass, but grass. Now do be quiet and let me sleep."

Next the boy split one end of a stick and used the forked end to pick fruit from the trees.

"Oh," wailed the trees from the garden, "wood presses against us again and again."

"Obviously," sighed the queen, "the boughs are rubbing against each other. Now do be quiet and let me sleep." So saying, she turned on her side and closed her eyes.

After the young son had picked the fruit, he mounted his horse intending to return home immediately. However, it occurred to him that he should not miss seeing the virtuous queen, even if it cost him his life. Quickly he entered the palace and made his way up the great staircase to the queen's chamber. Stepping into her room he went over to the golden bed where the queen lay sleeping in absolute peace. On her brow he saw a star and on her breast there shone a moon. Her waist was so small that just two fingers could enclose it. Golden hair streamed away from her perfect face. At her head and feet stood candelabra made of rare jewels. In the middle of the chamber was a table set for a feast. Crystal goblets brimmed with delicious beverages. Silver dishes containing the rarest foods were all about. First the youth tasted the dishes, then drank from the goblets, and finally he went over to the sleeping queen and kissed her three times on her pale cheek. She did not awaken.

Then with all haste the youth sped home.

After arriving at the palace, he went straight in to see the king.

"I greet you, Father," he said, and then handed him the saddlebags filled with rare fruit.

"I greet you also, my son," said the king. "Why do you return so late and wish to hurry away so quickly?"

"Father, I have been to the garden of the virtuous queen, and there I gathered the fruit for you. May it be the remedy you seek. If you become well, I shall return to the land of the virtuous queen."

The father touched the fruit and said, "Good, my son. My eyes will see again and my health will be restored."

When the virtuous queen arose, she noticed that someone had eaten her food and drunk from her goblets. When she went to the mirror, she saw a slight flush upon her left cheek and knew that she had been kissed. Quickly she ordered the grand armies of her seven realms to march to the country of the blind king. There, before the capital city, she pitched her forces and sent a messenger to the monarch.

"The queen demands to see the youth who picked her fruit," declared the messenger.

First the eldest son went out to meet her.

"Tell me, valiant sir," demanded the virtuous queen, "how did you pick the fruit?"

"With my hands, of course," said the boy.

"Impossible," replied the queen, "send me someone else."

Immediately the second son arrived.

"Tell me, worthy sir," the queen repeated, "how did you pick the fruit from my garden?"

The second son gave exactly the same answer and was rejected, too.

Now the youngest son was sent to see the queen.

"Tell me, young sir," she asked. "How did you pick my fruit?"

In exact detail the youngest son told her all he had done.

Immediately the queen kissed the son three times on the left cheek, and then she turned his face and kissed him three times on the right cheek.

"According to custom and practice, one has the right of double payment from thieves," she said.

Then they went arm in arm into the presence of the blind king. The queen held her hand over her face, and when she was in front of the old king she touched his eyes and his body with the same hand. Immediately, his health and his sight were restored. He became as strong as a lion.

Shortly afterward the marriage of the youngest brother and the virtuous queen was celebrated with great rejoicing.

Later, the couple was blessed with sons who resembled the father and with daughters who resembled the mother in every respect.

The Fish

This story from Australia is typical of the primitive folklore found throughout Southeast Asia.

ONG, LONG AGO THERE LIVED IN THAT REGION of the world now known as Australia two brothers named Naru and Masa. Now, as it happened, Naru was very clever while his brother was extremely stupid.

One day Naru carved a squid out of wood. It looked so real that he decided to throw it into the sea. Instantly it came alive and swam away. However, to express its gratitude to Naru, from that day on it drove a school of small herrings close to shore so that Naru might catch them easily and have plenty to eat.

After a while, Masa noticed that his brother had more than enough fish to eat for his supper whereas he, Masa, had scarcely any at all. Greatly curious as to how his brother managed to catch so many fish, he decided to question him.

"Where do you find so many fish, brother? Tell me so that I may go there, too."

"Masa, I will tell you a secret," replied Naru. "I carved a squid that looked so real that when I threw it into the water it became alive. Out of gratitude it has been driving the herrings close to shore so that I may easily catch them for my supper."

169

Thinking for a moment, he suggested, "Why don't you carve a fish too? But make *sure* that it is a squid," he warned with a severe tone in his voice.

Masa went home immediately and sat down to carve a fish. But because he was extremely stupid, he greed-

ily carved a barracuda instead of a squid, as his brother had suggested. As soon as it was finished, he threw the wooden barracuda into the water, and just like the squid earlier, the barracuda became alive. Immediately it swam toward the herrings and devoured them. Seeing this, Masa began to cry.

"What kind of fish did you carve?" demanded Naru angrily.

"A barracuda," sobbed his brother.

"You fool!" exclaimed Naru in despair. "Now your fish will eat up all the others and in the end he won't even spare us."

And that is exactly what happened.

Even to this day, barracudas attack fish and men.

The Turtle and the Rhino

*The common folk tale theme of brains over brawn
is given a new twist in this tale from Kenya.*

 HERE WAS ONCE A TURTLE WHO LIVED NEAR a stream because all around it grew delicious chives, the turtle's favorite food. One day as he sat on a broken tree limb sunning himself, he was astonished to see a rhinoceros emerge from the water and waddle toward land. As the turtle had never seen an animal so huge, he was quite terrified and quickly scurried under some leaves.

Not long afterward the turtle had a second terrible shock. While taking a bath in the stream, he looked up to find a huge elephant drinking water right next to him. He had never encountered an elephant before either, and now that he was aware that the world was inhabited by such very enormous creatures, he became quite worried. How could he protect himself against such strength? At last, being an extremely intelligent turtle, he devised a clever plan.

One day he went to the riverbed and called out to the rhino, who was contentedly lolling in the water:

"Dear friend, I just thought I should tell you. The elephant is going about everywhere, bragging that he's much stronger than you."

Surprised, the rhino raised his head. "Is that true?"

172

he asked, with a trickle of irritation in his voice.

"It's true," replied the turtle.

"And you believe it?" asked the rhino.

"I believe it," replied the turtle smugly.

"Well, then, you are indeed a very stupid turtle.

There is no one stronger in the whole forest than I. Who else can live for such a long period of time on either land or water?"

Slyly the turtle replied, "I beg your pardon; I am not stupid at all. It's you who are so stupid! Why, I wager I could personally best you in battle."

"What?" exclaimed the astonished rhinoceros. "How could a tiny creature like you best me?"

"Well," puffed the turtle, "if you don't believe me,

then let's settle the matter. I'll get a long rope. You pull from one end, and I'll pull from the other. If you succeed in pulling me into the water, then you've won the battle. If not, I shall claim victory."

This seemed reasonable to the rhino.

"All right," he said, "I agree."

"Good," said the turtle. "Exactly at noon tomorrow, be right here, at the river bank."

And he hurried off.

Quickly he went to the elephant's quarters and woke the poor beast up from a delightful nap.

"I have just left the rhino," gossiped the turtle, "and he claims he's much stronger than you. What do you think of that?"

"What?" said the elephant flapping his huge ears. "How can the rhino say such a thing? It's the most ridiculous thing I've ever heard."

"Not at all," replied the shrewd turtle. "Look, the rhino even gave me this rope. Tomorrow exactly at noon you are supposed to have a tug of war."

"Oh, for goodness sakes!" said the elephant, who was really a mild creature. "I don't believe a word you're saying." He had heard that turtles sometimes played tricks and that one shouldn't always trust them. Sleepily, he tucked one paw about his head and started to nap again.

"Well, if that's the way you feel about it . . ." sputtered the turtle, greatly offended, "I'll hold a tug of war with you myself. I do believe the rhinoceros is right. You may be big and make a lot of noise, but underneath you're just a sniveling coward."

"Really!" exclaimed the elephant with exasperation

as he watched from one eye the silly efforts of the turtle as he tried to stamp his tiny feet. "It's absolutely ridiculous. However, if it will satisfy you, I'll meet you tomorrow."

"At noon then, down by the river bank," said the turtle, smiling secretly. "When you see this rope pulled taut, then you start pulling at the other end. Just wait," he lectured sternly, "I'll teach you a lesson."

With that he toddled off.

The next day the lazy elephant lumbered down to the river bank and observed that the rope was taut. Immediately he picked it up and started to pull on it. The rhino, who was submerged deep beneath the water and held the other end, did the same. Concealed behind some shrubbery and watching the contest with great amusement was the sly turtle. Both the rhinoceros and the elephant were very angry with themselves and entirely astounded when they discovered that they could not budge the small turtle. For several hours they pulled on the rope, until at last they were both quite exhausted. Puffing and fuming, the elephant at last let go and toppled over on his side, utterly fatigued. When the turtle saw this he immediately left his hiding place and went to the elephant.

"Well, my friend," he laughed triumphantly. "*Now* do you see what I am capable of doing?"

The huge beast regarded the tiny turtle with utter amazement. Still breathing heavily and stretched out on the ground, he was unable to answer for some minutes. At last he said, "Tell me, little turtle, how did you manage to do it?"

"Very simply," answered the turtle, delighted to give

expert advice. "I merely buried myself very deeply into the ground."

"Yes ... yes ..." pondered the elephant. "That must be it. Very deeply in the ground ..." he repeated with wonderment.

"Well, I must go now. Goodbye," said the turtle. And quickly he scurried off, further down the river where the rhino was just emerging from the water. Shaking droplets from his eyes, the exhausted beast examined the turtle with surprise.

"It's true," he mumbled with confusion, "you are very small. Still, I am willing to tell the lion that of all the small land creatures, you are by far the strongest."

The turtle was more than satisfied with the results of the contest.

However, when the lion heard the story he suspected some trick immediately. He therefore told the turtle that before he could issue a certificate of strength he must test the turtle himself. The horrified turtle swiftly replied that much as he would like to, he was really too tired at the moment for another tug of war.

After that, whenever the lion challenged the turtle, the clever creature always had an excuse ready.

That is why up to the present day the turtle has still not received his official certificate of strength, and why most animals in the forest do not regard the turtle as a creature to be feared.

The Story of the Cuckoo

From New Guinea, a simple and fascinating explanation of why the cuckoo's egg-laying habits are so different from those of other birds.

ONG AGO, BEFORE MEN WALKED THE EARTH, there once was a forest god whose son died and went to the underworld. Calling all the animals together, the forest god asked them to sing songs of praise to his son as long as they were able.

Early in the morning the singing began, and continued all through the day and long into the night. One by one the animals and birds began to tire, however, and at last the only voice echoing through the forest was the loud clear tone of the cuckoo. On and on he sang, though trembling with exhaustion, until at last the forest god commanded him to stop.

"You have satisfied me," said the forest god. "Your devotion shall be rewarded. For such excellent service I permit you now and forever to lay your eggs in the nests of all other birds. You shall not spend your energy building nests, nor hatching eggs; that, too, will be the task of the other birds. Their duty shall be to take care of your eggs."

This is the reason why even today the cuckoo does not build a nest nor hatch the eggs of her own young.

The Rabbit and the Monkey

The effort of trying to control one's bad habits is humorously examined in this folk tale from the Congo.

NCE UPON A TIME A RABBIT AND A MONKEY were taking a walk in the woods. After they had gone a little way the monkey suddenly turned to the rabbit and said critically, "What in heavens name is the matter with you! Must you turn around every two minutes as though you were being followed?"

"Why shouldn't I?" the rabbit snapped back. "What business is it of yours! Besides, it's not half so annoying as the vulgar way you always scratch yourself."

Infuriated by this cutting remark, the monkey responded with a sharp retort. Before they knew it, the two friends were deep in the middle of a terrible argument. For hours they squabbled back and forth, first one winning a point and then the other. At last they decided to settle the matter. They agreed to meet the following day and sit together from dawn to dusk, during which time neither the monkey nor the rabbit would scratch himself or look around.

The next morning dawned bright and clear. Both friends hurried to the appointed spot and sat upon the grass facing each other. The rabbit conducted himself

most admirably, staring fixedly at the ground, while
the monkey with the very best intentions folded his
arms.

As the sun rose overhead and the day began to get
hotter, the monkey found it increasingly difficult not to

scratch himself. At last the torment became so unbear-
able that he decided to tell a story.

"Did I ever tell you, Rabbit," he began, "that when I
was in the war, I was hit by bullets many times? Here
and here and here and here—" Each time he pointed
out where the bullets had struck, he quickly and slyly
scratched himself so that the rabbit would not notice.

The rabbit by this time had grown terribly tired of
staring at the same spot of ground.

"When *I* was in the war," declared the rabbit to the monkey, "a terrible enemy pursued me everywhere. I was so frightened that I kept dodging back and forth, first this way, then that. I had to keep moving in all directions." As he described his war experiences, the rabbit suited the action to his words, moving his eyes all about with intense relief.

No one knows if the monkey and the rabbit continued telling stories until the sun went down, but one thing is certain—they surely didn't remain sitting still.

The Fisherman's Son

Because of his good feelings for all the creatures of this world, a simple lad receives greater rewards than he had ever dreamed of, in this enchanting fairy tale from Georgia.

NE DAY A FISHERMAN AND HIS SON WENT fishing at a large river quite a distance from their home. At the end of the day they had caught so many fish that they had great difficulty drawing in their net. As the fisherman inspected his catch he suddenly exclaimed to his son, "Look at this one! Have you ever seen anything like it?" In his hands he held up a most extraordinary scarlet fish, which glinted like an enormous jewel in the sunset.

"I am going home now to fetch the cart," said the fisherman to his son. "You stay here and take care of things until I get back. Above all," he warned, "keep a close eye on the red fish."

Some time after his father had left, the young son picked up the beautiful scarlet fish and caressed it fondly.

"It would be a wicked thing to kill such a fish," he thought. "I would rather set it free."

He cast the red fish swiftly back into the water.

The fish, however, did not immediately swim away as the boy had expected, but instead returned to the shore. Rising halfway out of the water, it called out to the fisherman's son:

"Thank you for your kindness. Since you have been so good to me, I shall give you a present. Take this bone," said the fish, removing one from his fin. "If you

are ever at your wit's end, come to the river bank and draw this bone from your pocket. Call to me, and I will come at once to help you."

Gratefully the boy thanked the fish and placed the bone in his pocket. Immediately, the fish plunged into the depths and disappeared.

Soon after, the youth's father returned. When he discovered that his son had thrown the scarlet fish back into the water, he was outraged.

"The devil take you!" he shouted. "I never want to see you again."

The fisherman's son, driven off by his father's anger, decided to head for the forest. Just as he entered it, he saw a deer running towards him gasping for breath and ready to drop with exhaustion. Close behind and preparing to capture him were several huntsmen and their baying hounds. The boy, taking pity on the deer, ran to him and threw his arms about him.

"Aren't you ashamed," he told the hunters as they drew up sharply, astonished at the sight of the boy and the deer. "Chasing an animal so cruelly! And a tame one at that. He's mine and I trained him."

The hunters, embarrassed by their mistake, mumbled an apology and hastily rode away.

When they had gone, the boy released the deer, whose eyes glistened with gratitude. Instantly it plucked a hair from its coat and gave it to the boy.

"Because of the good deed you have done me, I shall make you a present. If ever you are at your wit's end and need my help, take this hair from your pocket and call me. I shall come at once to aid you."

Carefully the youth placed the hair in his pocket and thanked the deer. In an instant the deer was gone, and the fisherman's son was on his way again.

He had not gone far when he suddenly heard a terrible clamor in the sky. Looking up he saw a pretty crane being chased by a ferocious eagle. Feeling sorry for the poor crane, the boy seized a stick and hurled it up at the cruel pursuer. The stick flicked the eagle's wing, alarming him so that he wheeled about and flew off in another direction.

The exhausted crane dropped down beside the boy

and lay for some moments upon the ground before he began to recover. When he breathed easily once more, he turned to the boy and spoke.

"You have been so kind to me," he said appreciatively, "that I want to give you something." Swiftly he plucked a feather from his wing. "Here, take this," he said. "Should you ever be at your wit's end and need my help, just take this feather from your pocket and call for me. I shall come at once." Before the boy could express his thanks, the modest crane flew off.

With great care, the fisherman's son added the feather to the other treasures in his pocket, and continued on his journey.

He had been walking less than an hour when he saw a little red fox running toward him in great panic. Directly behind him and closing the distance were a pack of greyhounds.

Feeling sorry for the little creature, he flung out his hand and quickly swept him up, placing him beneath his coat. The greyhounds circled around in confusion for a while, then gave up the chase and ran off. When they were out of sight the youth placed the fox gently on the ground.

The fox looked up at his benefactor gratefully and rubbed against his leg. After that he spoke. "Because you have saved my life," he said, "I want to do something for you in return." Immediately he pulled a long red hair from his tail. "Here, guard this carefully in your pocket. If you should ever be at your wit's end and need me, simply pull this hair out and call my name. I shall come to you at once."

"Thank you," said the fisherman's son gravely. And

he placed the hair carefully in his pocket. After bidding the fox goodbye, he started on his way again.

Before very long he arrived at a lovely castle where dwelled a beautiful princess. He spoke to several of the servants, who told him that the maiden was looking for a husband, but that she would only marry a man who could hide himself so well that she could not find him. Several suitors had tried and all had failed.

When the youth heard this, he decided that he, too, would ask for the princess' hand. He requested an introduction to the princess and was soon presented to her.

"Why have you come?" asked the beautiful maiden, who was indeed far lovelier than the young boy had ever imagined.

"I wish to ask for your hand in marriage," he replied.

"Very well," she said, "you may. But, you must agree to one condition."

"What is that?" asked the youth.

"You must hide yourself in a place where I cannot find you. If you fail, you must die."

The youth quaked when he heard the last part of the condition, for he certainly did not want to forfeit his life so young. After some reflection he answered the princess.

"I agree to the terms if you grant me one request," he said. "I must be permitted to conceal myself four times."

The princess thought this request rather odd, but she granted it because she found the young boy very handsome and charming.

Immediately, the boy left the castle and traveled to the river bank. There he drew the fish bone from his pocket and called out to him:

"Fish, fish, I need your help!"

Instantly the fish rose from the water.

"What is it, my friend?" he asked.

"I am at my wit's end," said the boy. "I must hide myself so well that the devil himself won't be able to find me."

"That is easily done, said the fish. "Hop on my back." Quickly the boy did so, and the fish plunged to the bottom of the river and swam until he came to a secret grotto where he placed the lad. Then the fish hovered at the entrance so as to conceal it.

In the castle the maiden called for her mirror and then sat at her table gazing at it for a very long time, trying to discover where the boy had hidden himself. At last, greatly astonished, she perceived him at the bottom of the river.

"Good heavens!" she exclaimed. "What kind of a fellow is this?"

The following day the fisherman's son proudly entered the castle and was taken before the princess.

"Well, did you find me?" he asked.

"What you have done," answered the princess, "is all in vain. I saw you quite plainly, sitting at the bottom of the river with the red fish floating before you, trying to conceal you from me."

"Heaven help me!" thought the boy. "What kind of a sorceress am I dealing with?"

Swiftly he left the castle and ran to the forest. There

he took the hair of the deer from his pocket and he
called out to him:

"Deer, deer, I need your help!"

In a moment the deer appeared.

"What is it, my friend?" he asked.

"I am at my wit's end," said the boy. "You must help
me hide myself so well that not even the devil will be
able to find me."

"That's easily done," answered the deer. "Hop on
my back."

As fleet as the wind, the deer carried the youth behind the ninth mountain and to a secret cavern behind
it. Then the deer crouched in front of the tiny entrance
so that no one could look inside.

Once more, at the castle, the beautiful princess
called for her mirror and gazed for a long time into its
depths. Her eyes hurt and her head pained dreadfully,
but she continued to stare until at last she perceived
the youth behind the ninth mountain hiding in a secret
cavern.

"Oh, no," she uttered in amazement, "How did he
manage to get there?"

When the youth appeared before her the following
day, he was quite sure that he had fooled her this
time.

"Well," he asked the princess, "did you find me?"

"What you have done," she remarked, "has all been
in vain. I saw you quite clearly, hiding behind the
ninth mountain in a cavern. There was a deer standing
at the entrance, trying to conceal you from me."

The youth was astounded by her knowledge and he
began to get worried. He left the castle in great haste.

This time he went straight to a large meadow. There he drew the crane's feather from his pocket and anxiously called to him:

"Crane, crane, I need your help!"

In a moment the crane flew down from the sky.

"What is it, my friend?" he asked.

"I am at my wit's end," exclaimed the boy. "Can you hide me so well that not even the devil himself will be able to find me?"

"Yes, of course. That's easily done," replied the crane. "Hop on my back."

Flying upwards toward the heavens, the crane concealed the boy in a pocket of a cloud and then hovered directly below it.

Again, the maiden in the castle called for her mirror and had it placed before her. For hours she stared into the glass but could not find anything. Her lovely eyes grew red with fatigue and her pretty forehead throbbed with pain. At last, glancing at the heavens, she suddenly saw the youth secreted in the pocket of a cloud.

"Good heavens," she cried out, "is he a magician?"

When the boy appeared before the princess the following day, he was sure that this time she had been unable to locate him.

"Well," he asked confidently, "did you find me?"

"What you did," replied the princess, "has again been all in vain. I saw you quite clearly, hiding in the pocket of a cloud with a pretty crane hovering just beneath you."

"Good grief!" exclaimed the boy to himself, stag-

gered by her knowledge. "What shall I do now? If she
discovers me the fourth time, I am lost."

Again he went forth from the castle, and this time he
journeyed until he reached the woods. There he drew
from his pocket the hair from the fox's tail, and he
urgently called out to him:

"Fox, fox, I need your help."

Instantly, the fox was at his side.

"What is the trouble, my good friend?" he asked.

"I am at my wit's end," declared the boy. "I am in a
terrible predicament. Unless I hide myself so well from
the keen-eyed princess who lives in the nearby castle
that she is unable to find me, she will have me put to
death. What shall I do? Can you help me?"

"Don't worry," the fox reassured him. "Everything
will be all right. Go to the princess right now and request a two weeks' respite. I will then conceal you in a
place where she will never be able to find you."

The youth went back to the castle as the fox had
advised him, and he asked the princess for a two week's
rest. This she politely granted him.

When he returned to the woods he discovered that
the fox had dug under the mountain upon which the
castle of the princess rested and had tunneled his way
until he arrived directly beneath the couch upon which
the maiden was sitting. Quickly, the boy hid himself at
that spot and waited.

Now the princess again called for her mirror and had
it placed before her. Carefully she searched the east
and the west, the north and the south. But try as she
might, she found nothing. Anxiously, she inspected the
heavens and then the depths of the sea—but still there

was no sight of the youth. Hour upon hour she gazed into the glass, considering every inch of it and repeating her inspection many times. Still she did not find him. At last she cried out in desperation:

"Come forward, you sorcerer! I cannot find you anywhere."

Swiftly the youth appeared before the princess, his face engulfed in a radiant smile.

"Where did you hide?" she asked, smiling also, for in truth she was not unhappy to have lost her bet to such a charming young man.

When the boy told her of his hiding place, the princess thought him extremely clever, and she was even more entranced with him.

The very next day the young couple was married. After a very elegant feast to which everyone was invited including the young bridegroom's animal friends, the keen-eyed princess and the fisherman's son settled down to a long and very happy life.

Who Is to Blame?

How one bad act precipitates another is the theme of this allegorical folk tale from Sumatra.

N A WARM, SUNNY DAY MANY THOUSANDS OF years ago, when all the animals in the kingdom were quite friendly toward each other, Mrs. Otter suddenly got an intense craving for some tender lobster meat. Remembering that near the cove she had seen some lobsters that were not quite fully grown, she decided to swim over to satisfy her appetite. Before leaving, she asked her friend the deer to keep an eye on her babies, so that while she was away nothing would happen to them.

"I am going to do some fishing," she said. "When I return I'll share my catch with you."

"That's all right with me," answered the deer.

Contentedly the otter swam away, feeling that everything was all right and that she had absolutely nothing to worry about.

It so happened, however, that as soon as she left, the war drums sounded throughout the forest. The deer, who was the "Chief Dancer" whenever war dances were held, immediately responded to the music and began her dance. Unhappily, in trying to perform this dance as well as possible, her feet accidentally landed on some of the baby otters and killed them.

When the mother returned a few hours later and discovered the tragedy, she screamed accusingly at the deer, *"Why did you kill my children?"*

The sorrowful deer tried to explain.

"Immediately after you left, the woodpecker sang his war song. I, in accordance with my duties, began my dance. While I was dancing I became so involved that I completely forgot about your babies and I accidentally trampled upon them when they came too near to me."

The otter, half-mad with grief, shrieked in rage, "The king shall learn all about this! I'll tell him what's happened! The king shall decide who's to blame, and he shall pass judgment on you!"

At once the otter went to the palace of King Sahab, and she demanded and received an immediate audience with the mighty monarch.

"Your Majesty," cried the otter, throwing herself down at the feet of the wise and mighty king, "this unimportant servant of your realm lies at your feet and begs for justice."

"What wrong has been committed?" asked the king gravely.

"The deer has murdered my children," replied the otter. "It is important that you judge her guilty." The king thought for a while and then said, "If the deer has done this deliberately, she shall be found guilty and judged according to the laws of this land."

The king asked that the deer be brought before them. When the deer arrived, the king turned to the otter and asked her to repeat her charge. When she had done so, the king questioned the deer.

"Is this charge true?"

"Yes, My Lord," the deer replied. "I have killed her children and I ask for forgiveness."

"Why did you kill her children?" demanded King Sahab.

"Your faithful servant killed them accidentally, Your Majesty. When I heard the woodpecker sing his war song, I, in accordance with my duties, began to dance, and unwittingly I trampled upon the children of the otter when they came too near."

Calling the woodpecker before him, the king asked, "Woodpecker, did you sing the war song?"

"Oh, Majesty, I did, because I saw the giant lizard put on his battle sword."

"Well, if that is the case," King Sahab replied, "the woodpecker is certainly not guilty, for it is his duty to sing the war song whenever he notices anyone preparing for battle."

The king next asked that the giant lizard be brought before the court.

"Did you put on your battle sword?" asked the king.

"Yes, Your Majesty."

"And why did you do that?" he asked.

"I prepared for battle because I saw the horned toad put on his armor."

When the horned toad was called before the court and asked why he had put on his armor, he stated that he had seen the crab arm itself with its mighty and dangerous three-pronged sword.

"And did you," asked the king of the terrified crab, who had no idea why he had been called before the mighty monarch, "did you arm yourself with your three-pronged sword?"

"Yes, I did," replied the crab, "but not before I saw that the lobster had placed his lance on his shoulder, in

the way that he does when he prepares for battle."

Now the lobster was called before the king.

"Lobster," the monarch said in a most solemn voice, "did you place your lance upon your shoulder, in such a manner that it would indicate that you were going to battle?"

"I did, Your Majesty," said the lobster gravely.

"And why did you do that?"

"Because," said the lobster, "I saw the otter approaching the waters of the cove with the intention of swallowing my young.''

"So that is how it all came about,'' mused the king.

Turning to the otter, King Sahab charged, ''Your case against the deer is without foundation. It cannot be upheld. You, Otter, are solely to blame for the tragedy that has occurred. And your punishment has already been delivered.''